ANXIETY AND MAGIC THINKING

Anxiety and Magic Thinking

CHARLES ODIER, M.D.

Translated by

MARIE-LOUISE SCHOELLY, M.D.

and

MARY JANE SHERFEY, M.D.

INTERNATIONAL UNIVERSITIES PRESS, INC.

New York

First published in French, *L'angoisse et la pensée magique.*
Neuchatel: Delachaux & Niestlé S. A.

Copyright 1956, by International Universities Press, Inc.

Library of Congress Catalog Card Number: 56-9335

Manufactured in the United States of America

CONTENTS

The three stages of social adjustment—The factor which induces magic thinking is anxiety—Loss of the ego—The magic power of malevolent representations

Part Two

THE EGO AND PRELOGICAL REGRESSION IN
NEUROSES

CHAPTER

TRANSLATOR'S PREFACE

Some time before the untimely death of the well-known French-Swiss psychiatrist and psychoanalyst, Dr. Charles Odier, it had occurred to us that some of his works with which we had become well acquainted might be of interest to English-speaking psychiatrists. His *Anxiety and Magic Thinking* seemed especially suitable for translation, since this work successfully bridged the gap between the psychoanalytic and Piaget's schools of psychological thought. It has been our impression that although Piaget's works were familiar to most students of psychology in this country, their influence upon American psychiatric thought was in general relatively slight. Such a translation, we felt, would therefore not only serve to introduce the American public to a profound thinker in his field, but also present some of the more significant contributions of Piaget in a manner in which they could be assimilated into American psychiatric thought, which is so dominated by basic psychoanalytic concepts.

Dr. Odier's unusual and fascinating personality profoundly impressed those who knew him, so that it is not surprising that his literary style is so highly individualistic as to make a translator's task difficult. Particularly his frequent use of artful French terms of his own invention constituted a special problem for his translators. In addition to these difficulties, Dr. Odier's unexpected passing prevented us from clarifying with him, as we had intended, some of the occasionally ambiguous passages in the book.

It seemed to us therefore that our best course would be to remain as faithful as possible, even at the expense of an occasionally too literal translation. We have striven most of all for clarity of expression, on the simple theory that the late Dr. Odier's stimulating ideas, if understandably presented, would stand for themselves, and would need no special ornamentation.

M.-L. S.

ANXIETY AND MAGIC THINKING

GENERAL INTRODUCTION

1. Mental Structure and Psychoneurosis

"Psychoneurosis" or "neurosis" are terms designating certain illnesses affecting psychic functions. These illnesses develop when the psychic functions are no longer unified but operate independently of each other. Thus ego functions may become dissociated from unconscious activity; thinking dissociated from affectivity; or the activities of the moral conscience dissociated from the underlying activity of the infantile superego.[1] If these psychic functions do remain related to each other, conflicts within themselves may arise. Hence the normal coordination of mental functions can be hampered or destroyed by such conflicts and antagonisms.

[1] Translator's Note: In what follows, Odier presents his concepts of mental structure which are at variance with the classic psychoanalytic concepts of the id, ego, and superego. The salient points for the reader unfamiliar with Odier's work to keep in mind are:

1. The term, ego, refers to the whole of conscious and observable psychic phenomena. Hence all conscious superego activities belong to the ego.

2. The child takes all his moral dictates from outside himself, thus forming his superego which is always infantile in character. With growth, part or most of these superego dictates evolve and mature into the *moral conscience*. In certain neurotic adults, infantile superego dictates persist relatively unchanged since childhood. Hence, the superego in the adult is always infantile and neurotic. This theme has been developed by the author in detail in his previous volume, *Les deux sources conscientes et inconscientes de la vie morale*. In translating, we will use the term, *infantile superego*, in order to avoid confusion.

3. The unconscious refers to the collective repressed memories. All areas and activities of the developing mind evolve and mature except those which remain in contact with or related to the repressed childhood experiences. These immature areas of the ego are the "regressed areas" and constitute the neurotic modes of reacting and thinking.

3

Psychoneurotic illnesses are more frequent than tuberculosis or cancer. Furthermore, a great many human beings suffer from borderline neurotic conditions. If they escape an actual illness, they are popularly called "nervous." The psychoneurotic and "nervous" individuals no doubt constitute the majority of the population. No one concerned with the public welfare can possibly be disinterested in a condition which so greatly disturbs interpersonal relations in social and family life and which has spread like an epidemic over civilized societies.

Symbolically a psychoneurosis might be compared to a building—a complex one whose internal structure has a shifting, moving quality. The upper floors may give way until they reach down to the levels of the lower floors, and the latter may be crumbling down, becoming part of the foundations. However, there can also be ascending movements from bottom to top, these movements succeeding or opposing each other. Rather than extending this analogy, let us examine the structure of the building. Unconscious processes form the invisible foundations. Their existence and activities result from the original repressions produced by the first conflicts between the child and his environment. In the adult, unconscious processes are mobilized by these original repressed tendencies. Discovered by Freud, the unconscious processes were studied further by his pupils leading them to the core of instinctive and affective life.

Returning to the analogy, this building is visible to everybody. Friends and relatives are often invited to visit—during business hours at least. But an odd peculiarity soon strikes the discerning visitor: the style of the lower and upper floors do not harmonize, the former being archaic and the latter, modern.

This building represents the "ego" of the adult neurotic; it is the body of the visible and appreciable psychic phenomena of which the patient is in turn agent and victim and which define what can be called the *life of the ego*.

In every psychoneurosis, without exception, a part of the total ego has regressed. The nature of this regressed area, the modalities of its operations, betray its origin and nature which are *infantile,* in the genetic sense of the term. Moreover, a regressed area owes its lack of development to the fact that it has remained in contact with the unconscious processes. This means that the regressed area has not participated in the mental development of the individual and has remained alien to the progress accomplished by the other parts of the self. The regressed area might be called: the neurotic zone of the ego.

Having said this much, we can now describe the upper floors of our building. They represent the healthy and fully evolved zones of the ego, whose principal functions lie in the adjustment to reality and social life.

A general principle can now be formulated. Without the existence and intervention of a regressed area in the ego, no neurotic symptom can become manifest. Furthermore, one always finds at the basis of these regressed neurotic areas one or several unconscious processes. However, if the unconscious processes are necessary as etiological factors, they are not sufficient to explain the process. Both unconscious processes and regressed neurotic zones of the ego make up the etiological factors of a psychoneurosis. The regressed part of the ego is formed by the persistence of an infantile mental structure upon which the formation and organization of the psychoneurotic disturbance depends.

For example, we may mention as the most fully studied and most demonstrable neurotic zone of the ego: a persistent *infantile superego.*[2]

To have the right to speak of a structure or activity as re-

[2] The reader is referred to our first work, *Les deux sources conscientes et inconscientes de la vie morale,* La Baconnière, 2nd ed., Chap. II. Of special interest are the sections referring to the relations between the superego of Freud and the moral realism of Piaget.

gressed, one must first demonstrate that its most essential aspects are present in the thoughts and behavior of the emotionally ill adult, and that its modes and characteristics are identical to those of a well-defined infantile developmental stage. This volume is dedicated to an attempt to demonstrate this thesis. The important psychic activities of the child have been well described by Piaget and his associates; their work has greatly facilitated my task.

Summary. We may conclude that three orders of functional relations contribute to the formation and regulate the evolution of a psychoneurosis:

1. The relations between unconscious activities and the ego. For instance, there can be a direct influence of the former on the latter. The activities proper to the ego are invaded and dominated by one or more repressed drives and fall under the influence of the unconscious. An example would be an impulsive attack of aggression against an authoritative figure or against a love object.

2. The relations between the unconscious processes and the regressed neurotic areas of the ego. For example, there can be conflicts between unconscious, repressed drives and an infantile superego.

3. The relations between the regressed part of the ego and the areas of normal ego activity (an "intra-ego" relationship).

We can learn about the genesis of this third order of functional neurotic relations from the study of dreams and of two well-defined types of psychoneuroses (phobias and the "neurosis of abandonment"[3]). Excluding the first two types of functional relations, the third order will form the *only* subject of this study.

[3] See Part III.

2. ADUALISM

The whole problem of infantile mental activity is dominated by two key concepts: the concepts of "adualism"[4] and of "realism." The phenomenon of adualism was first formulated by Baldwin, whom Piaget has often quoted. In its most general sense, the term means a confusion between self and others, between the subjective data of the self and the objective data of reality; in short, between self and nonself and vice versa.

"What is more intimate and more strictly 'individual' than the feeling of being one's self, different from all others? In a famous analysis, Baldwin showed that this feeling is in reality the result of interindividual reactions and is particularly due to the process of imitation. During his earliest years, the child is not conscious of his subjectivity and all reality exists on a single level because of the confusion between external and internal experiences. In the child, reality and the unconscious processes are hopelessly confused."[5]

In other words, until approximately the age of ten, the child is unaware that his mind, per se, exists and is also unaware of its functioning in coping with reality. As a result of this twofold ignorance, the child develops the *spontaneous belief that everything happens outside the mind*. Not being able to apprehend

[4] *A*-dualism, meaning the absence of dualism. (Trans.)

[5] I must limit myself to this quotation from J. Piaget's *La représentation du monde chez l'enfant*. Alcan, 1932, see pp. 4, 155, 450, etc. For more details consult the author's works, particularly, *Le jugement et la raisonnement chez l'enfant*, Delachaux et Niestlé, 1928.

Piaget notes three forms of adualism:

1. Confusion between the sign and the signified; for example the word and the thing it designates. Word and object are one. (Normally this disappears around the seventh or eighth year.)

2. Confusion between the internal and the external, i.e., the subjective and the objective. (Normally disappears around the ninth or tenth year.) This study is particularly concerned with this form of adualism.

3. Confusion between thought and matter, or thought and its object. Thought is *in* the object which it elaborates and represents, and is not independent of it. (Normally disappears around the age of eleven or twelve.)

its own functioning, the mind in itself conceives of nothing. At most it only registers phenomena. We may say that this belief is related to an inability to discriminate between the two opposite currents: that which comes from the outside to the inside of the mind, and that which goes from the inside to the outside.

During the early stages of growth, the child considers nothing to be internal to himself; he cannot conceive of anything as being subjective or objective. Everything is external to his mind —but not objective ("objectivity" does not define reality; it only defines the correct relationship between the subject and reality). Despite this constant exteriorization of phenomena, everything actually remains subjective, albeit, unknown to the child who ignores himself as a separate entity.

Summary. The principle inherent in adualism is the fusion of two distinct and separate things: consciousness and reality, self and phenomena external to the self. In this principle is implied a fundamental inability to distinguish between the subjective and objective elements of psychic life; or if one prefers, this inability to distinguish is the psychological basis of adualism.

Adualism can also be defined as an "undifferentiation." If the child cannot differentiate the state of consciousness from its contents, i.e., separate the perception and sensation of an outside object from the feelings and thoughts created in him by the object, it is because he ignores the existence of consciousness as a phenomenon. This unawareness precludes the acquisition of the well-known "sense of self," i.e., a clear-cut sense of personal and subjective identity. To ignore the existence of self implies the impossibility of comprehending the particular functions of the self.

The psychic apparatus works with data which at times are supplied by the external world and at other times originate within itself. These external and internal contributions give rise to what we call mental functioning. In the child, these data are perceived and are conscious, but the fact of mental functioning itself is not realized and escapes the child's awareness.

All this unawareness and inability to distinguish produce the confusions, the errors, and the conflicts with others and with the social milieu so characteristic of the small child.

3. PROJECTION AND INTROJECTION

The characteristic mechanism of the phenomenon of exteriorization or adualism is projection. To project is to localize outside the mind that which takes place in it. The child constantly gives us examples of this mechanism. He automatically attributes his ideas, wishes, or feelings to others or to any element of his reality, be it a doll or an animal (animism). He does this with so much genuineness and belief that he is unaware that the "reality" is only in his own mind. Therefore, projection means that an element of the self is placed onto the nonself. This is what Baldwin calls the "projective stage" in the growth of the child.

The opposite mechanism is introjection, which requires two steps: first, an external element is introduced into the self, and second, the self claims ownership of it. The two mechanisms of projection and introjection are not contradictory; they result from the same lack of differentiation of the self from the external world or adualism. This explains why the child borrows as easily as he lends and then confuses the loan with ownership. Baldwin considered imitation to be the source of introjection, and to be secondary to the development of projection. Brief as they are, these considerations are sufficient for our purpose.

One might ask why I felt compelled to review Baldwin's theory. My justification is that the three mechanisms, *projection, introjection,* and *imitation,* recur again and again in adult neuroses. Our patients harbor the same illusions as the child. Every thought originating in the self but attributed to others is considered as "coming from them." For example, if the patient experiences a sense of guilt because of a false accusation, he can experience the guilt as painfully as if he had indeed committed the crime. However, are such errors in the adult the same as in the child? Therein lies the crux of our problem, which we shall elaborate later.

When introjection involves the whole self and becomes permanent in character, it becomes *identification*. To identify oneself is to put a nonself in place of the self. (For instance, the little girl imitates her mother while playing with her dolls and this contributes to the development of the valuable maternal instinct.)

Whatever the degree and character of the three mechanisms (projection, introjection, and imitation), their basic source is in infantile adualism. According to Baldwin, it is in imitating others that the child by degrees becomes conscious of himself, proportionately as he becomes aware of his copying or being copied by someone else.

Baldwin sees two successive phases in the process of imitation:[6]

1. In imitating the behavior of others, the child becomes aware of his own behavior. This is the starting point for the sense of self. Prior to this time, the infant attributed to his inner psychic states and images the same characteristics and values that he attributed to physical perceptions. He made no distinction between body and mind. Both were externalized and placed on the same level. With imitation, he is urged and helped to correct this confusion. Thus the transition to a "subjective" stage begins, and from then on, the child becomes increasingly conscious of having a self identical to one of his kin.

2. However, as soon as the child's attention is directed to

[6] We transcribe here the summary which Piaget gave in *Le jugement moral chez l'enfant*. Alcan, 1932, p. 450.

himself as a separate entity, he becomes capable of the reverse process. Assuming for himself the behavior patterns observed in others, he learns at the same time to attribute to others the feelings and intentions which he is now aware of in himself. "If I can feel as they feel, they can feel as I feel." In this way, an "ejective" process is initiated. The alternating relationships between this twofold process of projection and introjection with imitation define all the psychic life of the child. In fact, after their mutual elaboration has been achieved, it is the ever-shifting relationship between projection and imitation that assures the balance between awareness of self and knowledge of others.

The psychotherapist cannot overemphasize the importance of the foregoing analysis by Baldwin. This shifting relationship is transposed in its entirety to the symptomatology of certain adult neuroses. It characterizes the general attitudes and the particular reactions of many patients with little self-awareness.

With these remarks, we have reached the central problem of this study: the relations between infantile psychology and the psychology of adult neuroses. The inquiries of Piaget and his followers provide sound arguments in favor of this study. Since the concept of "primary realism" constitutes the heart of Piaget's theories, a brief summary of these principles is indicated.

4. REMARKS ON REALISM

In philosophy realism is the doctrine opposed to idealism. Idealism has nothing to do with the "ideal" but is derived from the word *idea*. Idealism designates a theory supposedly able to resolve the problem of the nature of the external world. This theory affirms that the world is made up of ideas, that it exists only in our consciousness, in the function of the representations and images we have of it. But these representations are not at all ideas which are independent of the mind that thinks them. "In other words, idealism affirms that what we call the 'external world' is a manifestation of our mind and has no independent existence from our consciousness . . ."[7] Thus ultimate reality is our representations of the world and our principles of knowledge.

On the other hand, the philosophical doctrine of realism "affirms that the external world has an existence independent of our mind and consciousness."[8] Therefore this second doctrine, contrary to the first, attributes to external phenomena and things a "reality per se," independent of the mind which conceives them, and maintains that these phenomena would exist outside and without the mind.

There has been needless confusion between this philosophical concept of realism and Piaget's totally different concept of realism in infantile thinking. To Piaget, infantile realism defines the capacity to attribute one's own psychic qualities to objects and people and to accept such attributed qualities as *real*, as absolute. A little thought shows clearly that the young child is neither a realist nor an idealist in the philosophical and popular sense of these terms.

On the other hand, common sense and popular use also define realism as a belief in the existence of things as we perceive them. By stretching a point, infantile realism could be compared to this belief, however, on only one condition: that the child be conscious of believing that the world exists as he perceives it. Obviously, this is not the case.

There is still another use of the word, realism, which has added to the confusion. In the sense Piaget gave it, infantile moral realism defines a position that is radically heteronomous.[9] However, popular terminology gives it a quite different and almost opposite meaning. The "realist" is an individual who sees

[7] M. Gex, *Initiation à la philosophie*, p. 217.
[8] *Ibid.*, p. 222.
[9] Heteronomous means determined by things and events outside oneself. If moral realism exists, one takes all one's moral and ethical standards from others.

people and things as they really are. He can establish (clearly and skillfully) strict objective relations between people and things and will then exploit them. In a word, the "realist" is a person with a strong autonomy of the self. This popular meaning for the term definitely precludes its use in defining adult neurotic behavior. Considering only this phenomenon it would perhaps be safer to define moral realism as the *exteriorization of the moral conscience*.

To my mind, the term, adualism, proposed by Baldwin, has the advantage over Piaget's term, realism, in not lending itself to any such misunderstanding. Baldwin states only that the child is adualistic—does not distinguish between himself and the outside world; and in so doing, Baldwin establishes and defines a fact proper to the object of his studies, the child—without confusing this fact with a doctrine accessible only to an adult mind. Of course, the child is an adualist without realizing that he is one.

Piaget distinguishes between moral realism and intellectual realism in the child; to these two concepts, I wish to add a third form of realism: affective realism (see Section 7). In the adult then, neurotically determined morality and moral behavior (moral realism), infantile and neurotic thinking (intellectual realism), and infantile neurotic affectivity (affective realism) can be reduced to and encompassed by the general concept of *exteriorization*. Exteriorization may be more precisely defined as *an exogenic mode of determination*, and the term can be shortened to *externalism*.

The above considerations have the advantage of establishing a firm bridge between infantile psychology and adult psychopathology. The concept of externalism in the adult renders the concept of realism in the child more obvious and clear to the psychotherapist, and it facilitates the practical application of Piaget's ideas to the treatment of psychoneuroses.

In the so-called "moral neurosis," for example, where an infantile superego structure prevails, externalism is deeply rooted. It perpetuates in the adult with precision and perfect continuity the attitudes toward authority of the child under eight years of age, attitudes which Piaget calls moral realism. This simply means that an internal and autonomous moral conscience has not yet begun to function because it has not yet been formed.

NOTE ON INFANTILE REALISM AND ADULT EXTERNALISM

Despite the necessary caution in the use of neologisms, we are going to propose and maintain in this work the term, "externalism," for three reasons.

1. With our patients and with the public in general, experience shows that the word, realism, gives rise to misunderstanding.

2. Its use is contraindicated in the practice of psychotherapy. Our interpretations and explanations must correlate precise facts, easily integrated by the patient in his actual experience as he feels and explains them to himself. The concept defined by the term, realism, is too wide and abstract.

3. Piaget defined the concept of realism in relation to the mentality of the child for whom the realistic attitude is both normal and universal, manifesting itself always and everywhere. The term, realism, proposed by Luquet and taken over by Piaget, perfectly suits its object, the child. Not so with the adult where the term, externalism, is justified by the existence of new possibilities created by the disappearance in normal adults of the extreme realism of infantile thinking. If some infantile realism remains, it is in a selective and fragmentary way, limited to particular points and areas.

The term, externalism, is justified in the adult only. It defines the tendency for one's actions and reactions to be determined by others and not by oneself and one's own values. This is the clinical basis of inferiority complexes and certain forms of neuroses.

Self-determination obviously does not exist in the child. The findings of genetic psychology have emphasized the importance of self-determination in the adult. Self-determination always exists in those areas untouched by neurosis or in all activities which have escaped the influence of an infantile superego and of unconscious processes. This is a positive fact introduced by psychoanalysis which must be taken into account and which, to my mind, justifies the use of the neologism, externalism.

Summary. The term externalism is applied to an exact relation between a normal infantile feature and a special neurotic process which in the normal adult should disappear during adolescence. It is clear that externalism in the adult is not infantile realism; it is not a necessary or normal stage but an anomaly of mental evolution. Infantile realism persisting beyond later childhood becomes an abnormality which can occur in adolescents and adults, and only then does it deserve its name. The essential difference between Piaget's realism and our clinical concept of externalism lies in the fact that every adult, except those suffering from severe mental illness or mental retardation, has definitely ceased to attribute psychic qualities to objects, perception to the perceived, or thought to what is thought; in short, subjective qualities to their elements and their external factors. Knowing the nature of a psychic phenomenon, the adult no longer uses realism. (He does not "reify.")[10]

From the above considerations, therefore, we propose that the term, adualism, be substituted for Piaget's term, realism.

10 Piaget uses the verb, to reify. The word in English is too obsolete to have gained acceptance. (Trans.)

5. Piaget's Concept of Realism

Piaget's ideas and views are so rich and varied as to preclude the possibility of developing them here. I shall limit myself to an attempt to summarize as well as possible the important elements of his thinking.

Infantile realism means to attribute to every psychic phenomenon an immediate and absolute reality. Since thought and feeling adhere intimately to their object, since perception "sticks" to the perceived, these thoughts, feelings and perceptions undergo an exteriorization and become the "real objects" themselves. One can then say that the individual "reifies" his ideas, perceptions, and sensations in that he projects an absolute reality into them. Therefore Piaget refers to the realistic processes as the processes of "reification." As every psychiatrist realizes, the tendency to "reify" is evident in a number of neurotic symptoms and more than evident in dreams. The analysis of phobias and of the "neurosis of abandonment" in subsequent chapters will serve to illustrate this process.

Summary. Where there is realism in the child, there is externalism in the neurotic adult.

This distinction emphasizes the essential difference between the infantile and adult mode of projection. In the child, projection is related to the undifferentiation of the ego, to unawareness of the self; in the adult the same condition does not exist.

In the adult, projection is related to unawareness of the projected element and not to unawareness of the self. For example, after having repressed his aggression, an individual may attribute it to others. Such projection may then make a persecuted man of him and persecutors of others. This double investment is a classical example of adualism in the adult.

Another form of projection exists to which we shall often refer: the projection, not of the affect itself and its characteristics, but of its complement or "complementary attribute." Experiencing a certain emotion, the subject spontaneously attributes to an object (human, animal or inanimate) the corresponding emotion or that emotion which seems to him necessarily to be the complementary psychic attribute of his own feeling. For instance, if an anxious person is afraid of somebody, he blindly imputes to that person not fear, but hostile and aggressive intentions. Thus the ascribed "wickedness" is the complement of the fear of being the object of the other individual's "aggression." The wickedness justifies the fear and calls forth the projection.

Piaget has named this mechanism "projection of the like" "reciprocal projection" (see Section 17). However, this term can be misleading to the layman. He will tend to give "reciprocal" its common meaning, i.e., would spontaneously assume that the reciprocal of aggression is aggression itself and the reciprocal of fear is fear.

6. The Three Kinds of Realism

There is much more to adualism than Baldwin saw in it. And it is to Piaget's original researches that we owe our increased understanding of the meaning and importance of this concept.

On the basis of infantile realism, Piaget erected a general theory of wide implications. This theory is developed in his book *The Child's Conception of Physical Causality,* and in a series of papers to which I refer the reader. Here I wish to develop three of Piaget's categories of realism which are directly related to my topic.

"Realism of the first category (A) exists when the subject attributes to external reality those objects or traits that are actually subjective. A second type of realism (B) exists when the subject considers his own point of view to be absolute or unconditional. There is realism of the third type (C) when the subject considers objects or characters to have an existence per se, when in fact their existence depends upon other objects or characters or on the perspective in which they are viewed."[11] It follows that:

(A) is the opposite of objectivity.

(B) is the opposite of reciprocity.

(C) is the opposite of relativity.

One can see that these three forms of infantile realism exclude their three opposite attributes which characterize mature thinking.

I believe the first form (A) is clear. The common principle of the second and third forms of realism can be defined by two propositions:

1. In every relationship with others, there can be, always and everywhere, only one viewpoint (C).

2. It follows that there is a spontaneous tendency to ascribe to this unique viewpoint an absolute quality (absolutism). The affirmation of this quality is as irrefutable as its negation is refutable (B).

Since only one modality or viewpoint is admitted and conceivable, it follows naturally that verification is unnecessary and impossible because no second or third possibility exists. The existence of several possibilities creates the necessity for hypotheses and a respect for objective proof, but infantile realism is by nature the enemy of hypotheses and experimentation as well as of relativity of thought. (Without meaning to do so, I have just described certain typical ways of thinking found in the majority of psychoneurotics.) Thus the character of infantile realism can be summarily reduced to these two propositions.

On the level of ego functions, the numerous adult neuroses basically differ from infantile realism only in gradations and

[11] *The Child's Conception of Physical Causality*, p. 271.

details. This similarity must be of interest to the therapist. It is founded in the general principle of adualism with its three basic psychic phenomena of unawareness, absolutism and externalism. These three form a striking triad often observed in psychopathology. I know of few adult neuroses in which these three symptoms or attitudes are completely absent. Generally, in the course of treatment, they appear in inverse order to their genetic development. Externalism first appears and soon leads to the appearance of absolutism, which may then be so strong that objectivity, reciprocity, and relativity are totally absent. Analysis of these deficiencies usually holds the therapeutic process at the level of the ego for a long time. However, during this ego analysis, many of the deeper unconscious mechanisms are revealed or become quite apparent to the therapist.

7. AFFECTIVE REALISM

In the child, realism pervades all spheres of mental activity. Consequently, objects and modes of reacting vary from one field of this (mental) activity to another.

Only two categories of realistic activities engaged the attention of Piaget and his followers: the processes of *thinking* and those of *moral behavior*. Hence the two forms of realism whose study we can assume to have been completed are:

1. *Intellectual realism* (of thought, reasoning, words, intention, etc.). Intellectual realism possesses its own logic, called by Piaget *prelogic*. This prelogic is founded on the primitive and infantile conceptions of *precausality*,[12] conceptions whose manifestations and strength lie in their *magic implications*.

2. *Moral realism* which implicates the principle of absolute heteronomy.[13]

---

[12] Cf. *The Primitive Mentality*, by Levy-Bruhl.
[13] Moral realism is brilliantly analyzed by Piaget in *The Moral Judgment of the Child*, 1932.

In an earlier volume,[14] I emphasized the interesting fact that the neurotic superego is formed by those moral principles which earlier made up the infantile realistic moral attitudes.

Comparable to the concept of the superego advanced by Freud for the first time in the history of mankind, the concept of moral realism is without question one of Piaget's foremost contributions. It would be fair to say that in their studies in the sphere of the superego these two masters have come closest to each other in their thinking.

The researches of the genetic school of Geneva have especially clarified the intellectual aspects of realism. Piaget's analyses, however, have only indirectly touched on the realism of instinctive and affective phenomena. But the realistic way in which the child experiences his feelings and reacts to his desires and fears is identical, in principle, with the manner in which he thinks and reasons. His affective realism is no less certain a fact, and perhaps a more important one, than his intellectual or moral realism. To understand the meaning of affective realism, one need only to transpose to the world of the instincts, needs, feelings and emotions of the child the principles applied by Piaget to the world of thoughts, reasoning, and judgments.

The infantile realistic tendencies utilized by affectivity are especially striking in the relationships which tie the small child to his parents and educators. These relationships form the first, and therefore the decisive, stage in the child's social evolution. Indeed they dominate the whole problem of the formation, structure and preservation of the famous feeling of security.

Affective realism can be considered an essential aspect of the child's life since he imagines all his joys and sorrows to be due to external causes and all his happiness and unhappiness to be dependent on the intervention of the human beings and things

[14] *Les deux sources conscientes et inconscientes de la vie morale,* Chap. III.

around him. The genetic school, however, seems to have neglected this aspect of the problem.

To my mind, affective realism must be given as much consideration as intellectual and moral realism. These three together form a genetic whole and should not be separated. All three are the direct result of adualism. One of our theses will be that the projection and introjection of the contents of consciousness exert their dynamic influence with more harm in the sphere of infantile affectivity than in the sphere of thought and intelligence. Affective realism is the most eloquent witness to the unawareness of self or the undifferentiation of the ego. The interference of affective realism seems to me both more clear-cut and longer lasting than that of intellectual realism. It extends into the area of moral realism until the time of puberty.

At any rate three clinical facts should now engage the attention of the genetic psychologist as well as the psychoanalyst.

1. In the adult, if moral realism (externalism) is traced to its source, it is found to proceed directly from infantile affective realism. At the source of human morality is affectivity as well as affectivity's chief component: the need for security. "Moral ideas" come much later; in childhood they are the by-product of emotions. This derivation is evident in the "moral neuroses." Affective and moral realism are so intimately related in the beginning that, if they survive adolescence, they remain so.

2. Actually, affective and moral realism frequently do survive adolescence. They offer a remarkable resistance to the progress of the mind and seem to defy its goals of maturity and complete differentiation. In some cases, the subject remains fixed at an infantile level; others regress to earlier levels only after traumatic circumstances. These processes are characteristic of the "moral neurosis" and the "neurosis of authority."

3. I shall call the third fact the phenomenon of *realistic differentiation*. In many subjects who have not gone beyond gram-

mar school in their education, definite signs of intellectual realism may persist. In the more educated individuals, there are only vestiges, insignificant or episodic traces of intellectual realism.

However, very educated and intelligent patients can exhibit to perfection infantile realism in their affective life or in special areas of it. In some instances, especially in the area of sexuality, one can observe the astonishing fact that the more intellectual development progresses, the more affective development regresses, often to the point of retreating to its earliest positions. The dissociation can be nearly complete and is, of course, of a pathological nature. The dissociation of affectivity characterizes many cases of the neurosis of abandonment. The defeat inflicted by infantile affective realism seems to be the price for the victory won over intellectual realism.

8. The Seven Difficult Stages

From this survey, condensed as it may be, a general principle can be elucidated which explains the development of the mind from the infantile state to maturity. According to Piaget's theory, the ego develops little by little out of the obscurity of unconscious adualism to the clarity of thinking which perfect knowledge of oneself gives to consciousness.

This evolution comes about in stages. Each stage corresponds to a victory over the existing forms and demands of infantile realism. Only after all his illusions about reality have disappeared can the human being justly flatter himself at having attained the peak of his development.

To reach this ultimate stage in development all the manifestations of realism have to be corrected and all their traces to be eliminated. This long process of healthy growth and development must reach all spheres of the mind's activity, including, of course, affectivity. The success of this process is often jeopardized by the violent interventions of instinctual needs, in general, and of sexual and aggressive impulses, in particular.

Anyone who concedes the genetic theory the value it deserves must recognize that this is an original definition of the ultimate goal of psychological evolution in human beings.

The end result of this process is identical with the greatest development that consciousness can achieve. And this process is not a gradually ascending walk through life, but a very steep and difficult climb. The overcoming of infantile realism takes place in two main stages, the first of which has been described by Piaget. He clearly outlined all its pitfalls and difficulties. Human beings pass through this stage of their development to maturity during late childhood, approximately from the sixth to the twelfth year.

This first stage of Piaget is characterized by four difficult phases. Intellectual realism must progress:

1. to objectivity
2. to reciprocity
3. to relativity.

Moral realism and heteronomy must progress:

4. to the development of a self-determined moral conscience.

These are the difficult psychological tasks that burden late childhood. Not to help the child with these tasks during the very critical period of puberty is to lead him on the path of neurosis.[15]

Each recoil of realism marks a new advancement of the ego; the final defeat of realism leads to maturity and guarantees the equilibrium of adult life.

It is in the analysis and description of the second stage that I should like to contribute my own concepts.

Nature, morality and society have, so to speak, signed a pact

[15] The most formidable obstacle in this process is the essentially realistic attitude of the guilt feelings which arise during this critical period.

according to which young people have to achieve their freedom from immaturity during the adolescent period.

This means that between twelve and twenty years of age adolescents must build their personalities on solid bases, and later achieve an integrated organization of the self. In this period, they meet three obstacles or three more difficult phases, no less rugged than the first four. This makes a total of seven "difficult passages."

The last phase of evolution consists of passing healthily from affective realism:

5. to the acquisition and preservation of the sense of internal security (the process of endogenous security or *securitization*),

6. to the acquisition and preservation of the sense of internal self-value (the process of endogenous *valorization*),

7. to the acquisition and preservation of the sense of autonomy or independence (the process of endogenous *autonomization*).

Like the first four, these last three processes contribute to the liberation from infantile realism. All seven together make up and define ego organization. The last three accomplish the complete liberation from externalism, resulting in a clear consciousness of an absolute dualism.

To reach the stage of dualism is to acquire a clear and objective concept of the self and of its relations to the "nonself."

Thus the fifth, sixth and seventh passages will be the principal object of this analysis of psychogenetic development. The fifth will be the theme of this volume; the sixth and the seventh will appear in subsequent volumes.

As we have just outlined it, healthy organization of the ego presupposes the success of a series of very delicate operations. Moreover, this success implies the absence of unconscious complexes and the lack of dynamic repressions.

Two groups of patients have difficulty in achieving the last three stages. They lose their balance; their resources and security fail them; and they relapse into realism easily. These patients suffer from (1) inferiority complexes or the neurosis of insecurity with self-devaluation; (2) various phobias; and particularly (3) the neurosis of abandonment.

To pass successfully through these three stages insures a safe escape from these painful illnesses or an effective immunization against them. In any case, the achievement of the feelings of security and self-esteem has been accomplished. There remains only to organize these feelings into a stable and permanent part of the personality. This final process leads to full socialization; and finally the individual acquires the valuable quality of *autonomy* which is indispensable for an appropriate social behavior and is essential for a healthy moral conduct.

9. THE EGO FUNCTIONS
THEIR RELATIONSHIPS TO THE MENTAL FACULTIES

Having accepted these three developmental processes as essential to healthy mental growth, one feels obliged to formulate a theory about them. For this purpose, I shall group them into a functional whole having the value and role of a regulating system. In this system, each element is regulated by the action of the others. In order to clarify this statement it is essential that these elements be defined in precise terms.

I have decided to name these three processes (security, valorization and autonomy) the *ego functions*.

The necessity for this new terminology cannot be denied. These three processes as a whole originate in the ego, belong to the ego, and obey the ego's functional laws. Their main function is to combat infantile realism and rid the mind of it. Besides this, they contribute to the regulation of "ego well-being" by maintaining its level. When the sense of well-being decreases, this regulation assures the efficiency of the ego's activities and its adjustment to reality.

Two hypotheses can be formulated about this system of triple action: either its formation is inherent in the general development of the human mind and common to all human beings, or it can be a secondary (actually a belated) reaction against the state of dependency and inferiority to which realism has condemned the child. In any case, it is certain that the triad is correlated with the progress of consciousness in establishing the stability and permanence of the related feelings of security and self-esteem. If I am not mistaken, the ego functions form a well-defined system. The three processes which compose this system are related in such an intimate way that they may be considered to be one and the same process.

It is important to distinguish between this functional system and a second system, *the system of the faculties.* (The term is used in its traditional and current sense, referring to intelligence, reasoning, will power, memory, etc.) The mechanism and goals of these two systems are obviously very different. Each obeys its own laws and pursues its own ends. However, it is essential that they coordinate their functions and harmoniously adjust to each other's operations. This functional synergy is the necessary condition for the individual's emotional balance as well as for the success of his adjustment and accomplishments. On the other hand, disorders in their interrelations and disharmonious functioning cause disturbances and anomalies characteristic of the neuroses of inadequacy and inferiority.

Let us conclude this first outline of my working hypothesis with a summarizing thesis: In a great many adults, the decline of realism does not result in its complete disappearance. Although apparently overcome and outgrown, realism remains latent in some psychic spheres. It is characteristic of some neuroses that this latent realism is rendered manifest and produces symptoms.

The memories of the earlier realistic tendencies must have remained deeply embedded in our minds; we could not have invented them.

Neurosis does not create these realistic tendencies; it reproduces them. The neurotic symptoms of the ego are not an original experience for the individual. Technically, there is no new morbid formation, but one or more areas of the self regressed to an infantile level. Going a little beyond my thesis, there could be no neurosis without realism; there could be no externalism without neurosis.

10. THE COMBINED METHOD

Freud used to ask himself: Why are my patients' symptoms derived from the psychological disturbances they had in childhood? Why do their fantasies and dreams have infantile themes? On the other hand, how can a child suffer from psychic disturbances, especially obsessions, phobias, and nightmares? Where does the child's anxiety come from?

The correct answer to these questions could be given only by the exploration of the unconscious. This original method of Freud's threw a vivid and unchallenged light on the instinctive and affective life of mankind.[16] Hence Freud's chief interests remained with the instinctual and affective life, and his goal was to define its vicissitudes. He determined the three original stages of libido development (oral, anal, and genital or oedipal) and the phases of aggression (masochism, sadism, combativeness, rivalry, etc.). Then going to the very depth of the human psyche, he at-

---

[16] An "affect" is that which "affects" the mind. This term condenses two ideas so closely related that they are practically one. First, a psychic energy of an affective and unconscious nature and, secondly, the effects on consciousness of the activity of this energy. For example, a vivid feeling of fear or anxiety is the effect on consciousness. Neurotic anxiety is the most ubiquitous morbid affect. Thus an affect has a double character: dynamic and qualitative. In psychiatric thinking since Freud, instincts and affects have come to constitute a kind of functional and etiological unity.

tempted to determine the source of anxiety. It is important for
our purposes that the Freudian theory of anxiety be extensively
analyzed.

Piaget, on the other hand, asked himself a different set of
questions. How does the child emerge from adualism and how is
he later able to grasp the existence and essence of his own self?
After what awakenings of consciousness does he reach the point
where he affirms dualism through recognizing himself as different from all the other selves with whom he had identified as well
as similar to those others into whom he had unconsciously projected himself?

Piaget's main interest is "the life of the ego," and more exactly
the evolution of infantile consciousness as related to the development of thought. He determined all the stages through which intelligence has gone. The last of these stages is the acquisition of
logical and conceptual thinking, along with formal thinking.
The problem of ego formation dominates all his researches.
Piaget's keen analyses finally led him to grouping the first stages
into one category which shows a prelogical character of mental
operations. Prelogic is the opposite of logic. Piaget grouped the
last stages into a second category called the logical phase of the
development of thinking.

According to this interpretation, logic has two objects: on the
one hand, it is concerned with ideas and reasoning and thus
depends on the mental faculties. On the other hand, logic is concerned with the social relationships. This social logic has been
called by Piaget the "logic of relationships" and depends on the
ego functions. It rests in part on the principles of objectivity,
relativity, and reciprocity; and in part on the social feelings
(solidarity, cooperation, mutual respect, etc.).

But Freudian psychology pointed out an important phenomenon. In many cases, mental logic and social logic are not acquired coincidentally. As we know, adolescents become familiar

first and most easily with the principles and laws of intellectual logic. The logic of interpersonal relationships, the necessity of applying this logic to family and social life, may escape them for a long time. (The fact that this timing is not coincidental inevitably produces a lag, and later a dissociation, in personality development.) Intellectual and affective development do not always proceed simultaneously; and the resulting lag remains the specific feature of many adult neuroses. The discrepancy is a consequence of the vicissitudes of the pubertal crisis.

In some more severe cases, social logic remains forever alien to the mind; on this one important point the patient has never reached adulthood. He remains blocked by abnormalities of the last two categories of ego functions: valorization and self-autonomy.

In itself, autonomy of thought is only half the battle. It must be paralleled with the autonomy of the affective life (needs, emotions, feelings, etc.). These two processes of evolution achieve full success only if they are intimately correlated. However, a third process must intervene if success is to be achieved: the formation of a *sense of subjective responsibility*.[17]

The sense of subjective responsibility has two objects:

1. ideas, reasoning, opinions, decisions (intellectual responsibility);

2. instincts, affects, and feelings (affective responsibility).

The adolescents' task is to experiment with their desires and feelings and to assume responsibility for them, especially when they motivate their preferences and choices—and to do this not only because of social demands but out of a sense of inner obligation.

It is at this step that adolescent dissociations most frequently occur. A young man may be able to reason most effectively but has not yet acquired any sense of his affective responsibility. In

[17] Which must be substituted for the earlier sense of objective responsibility inherent in realism and described by Piaget.

the presence of young girls, he possesses neither ease nor simplicity, but is either shy and embarrassed, or rude and disdainful. He takes flight or is aggressive. With his mother, he is distant and cold. She complains bitterly that her "John is all changed—he who was so sweet and affectionate." John escapes her. She does not understand that he is shielding himself while trying to free himself. In college, John is a brilliant student. In short, intellect has separated itself from affect. Carefully cultivated in college, the intellect continues to develop satisfactorily, whereas in his home, his affective life remains enveloped in infantile realism. Parents should handle this behavior with understanding. It is essential to the healthy evolution and synthesis of the personality that affective responsibility be achieved. It is a prime requisite for success in love and marital life.

These brief remarks open a whole new aspect in the field of ego pathology. Delays and inconsistencies in the affective evolution are characteristic of youth and plant the seeds for a neurotic development. They seem more and more frequent in our present period of social crisis and play an enormous role in psychopathology.

Sketchy as they are, these are some of the essential lessons to be obtained from the works and ideas of Piaget. These works can be supplemented by further research of psychopathologists and gain additional strength and verification.

Carried on by the irresistible impulses of his fruitful researches, and like Freud, inspired by so many original discoveries, Piaget finally erected his vast theory of the realistic system. He analyzed this system into all its parts—except the affective sphere—and reorganized it into a coherent whole of remarkable unity. Piaget made himself the famous exponent of logical thinking and knowledge. He became the great exponent of the importance of the concept of the self; whereas Freud became the great exponent of the unconscious. The latter in the genetic sense is synonymous with repression, and repression is the result of affective conflicts, not intellectual ones.

The favorite topic of psychoanalysis is the *formation of the unconscious;* with the genetic psychologist, it is the *formation of the awareness of self,* of the *ego.*

But only as objects of study can the unconscious mind and the ego be separated. These psychic functions are inseparable in the living experience of any human being. In the neuroses, the unconscious and the ego are in constant conflict. Nothing can tie two people who dislike each other or two antagonistic processes more intimately together than the conflicts between them. And this is more true during personality development than at any other time.

After analysis comes synthesis. On the one hand, we have two teachers, two schools, two doctrines; on the other hand, the psychic life, the living child and man. On both sides the positive aspects are the enormous work accomplished, final results recorded, essential facts learned. The negative aspect remains the lack of synthesis.

The psychoanalysts have somewhat neglected the study of the laws of thought and intelligence and the evolving modes of the formation of the mind. The genetic psychologists have neglected the characteristics of affectivity with its origins and functionings. They have treated instincts and emotions like poor relatives— while the analysts have given the affects overwhelming attention and revealed their unsuspected riches to the astonished scientific world.

However, in the face of the sensational discovery of the importance of the oedipus complex and the superego, scientific honesty requires that infantile realism be given the attention it deserves.[18] On the basis of these considerations, we can conclude

---

[18] Freud and Piaget themselves did not suspect that the oedipal situation and infantile realism are related to one another by genetic bonds.

that the strongest aspect of the Freudian doctrine is the weakest of Piaget's doctrine, and vice versa.

Psychoanalytical and genetic schools have a common, fundamental object of study: the psychological evolution of the human being. Comparing the evolution of the individual to a river, I should say that Freud and Piaget both ascended it to its source—but each on his own bank. By definitions, this parallelism condemned them never to meet.

I believe it is high time that we throw some bridges across the river joining the intellectual and affective banks. At the very least, we need a large bridge at every turn of the stream, that is, at every well-defined stage of psychological development. The child is an organic whole. During childhood more than adolescence, and during adolescence more than adulthood, thought and affectivity are intricately interwoven. They are but two aspects of one and the same growth process.

In the work of Freud and Piaget, we have today two sources of information at our disposal—and do not have the right to discard either of them by invoking doctrinal prejudices. Psychoanalytic and genetic methods have brought us different but equally valuable data. The problem is to examine them with sufficient objectivity to be able to comprehend their interrelations and, if possible, achieve their synthesis.

Such a comparative study will prove that the respective works of these two schools complement and enrich each other. Freud apprehended the deeper energies of affective life and followed their transformations and destinies. Piaget outlined the machinery which operates these energies and regulates their functioning. Neither is separate or distinct from the other. The emotions pervade every aspect of life, and it is up to logical thinking to use them in good and healthy ways. Every psychology that wishes to be clinical and analytic must also be genetic. Both methods must be used and then combined into what may be termed the *genetic-analytic method.*

In conclusion, the new approach of this study lies in the synthesis of psychological and clinical facts. Essentially, it utilizes Freud's great formulations of the development of the oedipal situation and the superego as well as Piaget's concept of primary realism and Baldwin's ideas on adualism.

PART ONE

PHOBIAS AND NIGHTMARES

CHAPTER ONE

THE ORIGIN OF ANXIETY

11. The Freudian Theory of Anxiety.
Anxiety and Insecurity

The basis and inspiration for this study lies in a psychological fact observed in the course of treatment of numerous patients by the psychoanalytic method. This observation concerns the intimate relationship between anxiety and insecurity.

From the clinical viewpoint, the internal perception of a state of insecurity is a highly complicated phenomenon, an affective experience rather than an intellectual one. With many individuals of a special affective constitution and a certain degree of sensitization to insecurity, it becomes a pure feeling, devoid of any content, and not subject to objective verification. In quality and intensity this feeling possesses all the characteristics of a well-defined emotion. This emotion is then termed anxiety.

In a very large number of cases and situations, it was evident that the cause of anxiety, often the dominant and even determining factor, was nothing but insecurity. One may then ask whether it is necessary to look further for the origin or genesis of the anxiety? Every analyst and student of Freud faces this question because it was Freud who was the first to attempt a heuristic investigation of this nature. Such an investigation starts in psychology and ends in biology. In a remarkable speculation, Freud created the "biology of anxiety." In order to verify this speculation he had to go back to the origins of things, to the genesis of affects in infancy. What follows is a brief summary of Freud's famous theory.

37

In his first series of papers, Freud traced anxiety back to feelings of guilt, and guilt to the oedipus complex; he then believed that he had exhausted the analysis and revealed the deeper meaning of anxiety. Some twenty years later, however, on the basis of broader views derived from greater experience, Freud reconsidered his early theories. Looking beyond the oedipal situation and searching for psychic causation and instinctual origins, he encountered anxiety everywhere. He found its pathological influence at the earliest and most primitive levels of psychic experience. Carrying his investigations still deeper he discovered that this emotion, which is a universal characteristic of the human species, is as primitive as any biological phenomenon can be. In this deep analysis, the nearer he came to the source of anxiety, the more intense it became; and he was finally led from level to level to the birth of the child and even a little beyond. His attention had been attracted to a particular type of dream which he called "birth dreams." In their form and content, these dreams were always identical: an escape through too narrow a passage.[1] Here was indeed an anxiety-producing theme from which few of his patients escaped at one unpleasant moment or another in their treatment.

Hence, the origin of anxiety was related to birth, and preceded the oedipal period. The latter only used it; or more correctly, during the oedipal period, the earlier anxiety is revived in relation to feelings of guilt connected with the first sexual drives, expressing most adequately the incestuous character of these drives. Thus a preoedipal form of anxiety existed which had nothing to do with morality and all to do with biology. Rank, one of the early but later dissident disciples of Freud, developed this theory systematically to the point of raising it to a general concept of human life. The facts upon which Rank

---

[1] Etymologically, the word anxiety, is derived from the Latin, *angustiae*, meaning a narrow passage or gorge.

based his theory are not devoid of interest and objectivity but would have been more convincing if he had refrained from changing the facts to fit his personal convictions. As so often, the disciple went beyond the master's concepts and even misinterpreted them.[2]

Freud published his new theories in *Inhibition, Symptom and Anxiety* (1926). The reading and study of this paper was one of the most inspiring moments of my life as an analyst. Nothing impressed me more than his ease in these obscure depths and the light he threw upon them. Later when I discovered Piaget's book, *The Moral Judgment of the Child,* I was struck by the unquestionably profound relationship between these two masterpieces. The present work is the result of my comparisons and reflections on these two themes treated from their two different viewpoints.

Biologists and obstetricians would agree on one point: apparently the process of the expulsion of the fetus from the uterus combines all the physiological conditions necessary to produce a state of anxiety. An adult subjected to similar physiological stresses would probably die. A situation more suited to create a feeling of mortal insecurity cannot be imagined. Indeed our patients' birth dreams daily convince us of this fact, they awaken from them submerged in anxiety and cold sweats.

The theory of birth anxiety, however, raises a very pertinent objection. Has this traumatic event really been lived through by its victim, the child? Has he realized the anxiety which we, as adults, impute to him, suppose him to suffer? To put the question is to answer it. A fetus is not able to convert the event, be it ever so sensational, into an experience. Sensational it is, indeed—for the mother, but not for the infant!

The infant's consciousness loses nothing in the delay of its capacity to experience anxiety. We might say that anxiety only

2 O. Rank, *The Trauma of Birth.*

waits for consciousness to awaken in order to invade it. Nervous children have anxiety attacks from their second or third years on. These often reach the pathetic intensity of phobias. The child's consciousness of anxiety is then quite evident. Indeed it is these children's misfortune to realize anguish at so early an age. The concurring testimony of so many troubled mothers is as significant as all the scientific theories they confirm.

We can easily understand why some biologists raise the question of this infantile anxiety—whether it is primary or secondary to the birth anxiety—and have sought to determine its origin and nature. Such an investigation rightly conforms to their aims and purposes and is not a problem for psychology. To the psychologist, anxiety deserves the name only at the moment it acquires a character and quality that is properly psychic. We do, of course, know that the physiological elements of anxiety can never disappear. The most unquestionable psychogenic anxiety attacks are regularly accompanied by unpleasant sensations localized in almost every part of the body, and especially in the chest. The common language often uses the word "oppression" to describe the feeling of anxiety, and there could be no better word for it. In this connection, anxiety is a perfect example of a mixed affect.

One fundamental fact could not escape Freud's astute observations. Anxiety may originate in the body and its physiological apparatus (somatogenic), in the psychic apparatus (psychogenic), or in both, either simultaneously or successively. In all three instances its manifestations are identical and hence seem independent of its origin both in practical significance and theoretical value. This functional identity struck Freud forcibly.

From then on, he believed he was on the right track. He had established a fundamental and precise relationship between the biological and the psychological spheres. To support psychological investigations with biological arguments is to render them more accurate and to avoid purely speculative interpretations.

There is little enough precision in the field of psychological research; established facts are too rare, and speculative theories only too numerous.

From this time on, Freud based his second theory of anxiety on this fundamental relationship.[3] Today this concept is considered the authentic "Freudian theory of anxiety." Briefly, this theory rests on the existence of three etiological factors, all of which must be present.

At the basis of anxiety is the feeling of danger, the *primum movens*, which starts the process and remains so to the end. However, before the ego can experience true anxiety, two other conditions must exist. On one hand, there must be a feeling of complete helplessness in the face of danger (*Hilflosigkeit und Ratlosigkeit*). On the other hand, there must be the recollection or sudden evocation of a painful memory: a memory of an identical situation which has previously occurred one or many times and has turned out badly for the inexorable reason that the subject was totally unable to master the situation with his own psychological powers or to resolve it with his own resources. This past situation, the memory of which unavoidably invades consciousness, lends the experience a poignant reality. The past situation is both dangerous and highly traumatic in that it gives the subject the sensation of having lived through a "trauma."[4]

These two conditions, once experienced, help to produce a specific feeling: the paralyzing feeling of an imminent catastrophe which becomes the immediate cause of anxiety. Around this feeling, a gripping fear crystallizes in consciousness.

These are the three affective factors which form the "psychic

[3] In the earlier theory, anxiety was considered a transmutation of "sexual libido." Too great a quantity of unused and unsatisfied libidinal energy created a corresponding quantity of anxiety.

[4] Meaning a shock or wound which breaks the psychic equilibrium, paralyzes or dissociates consciousness, leaving profound impressions. If such a wound be healed, it can no longer be considered a trauma in the Freudian sense.

tripod" of the Freudian theory of anxiety. Together they form a functional unity: danger—helplessness—a memory. Obeying his deep concern with and need for synthesis, Freud founded his remarkable theory on this three-dimensional genetic relationship.

Summary. There can be no psychic trauma without a feeling of powerlessness real or remembered. There can be no feeling of powerlessness without a feeling of danger.

It follows that anxiety is a reaction of the ego to a coherent whole of exogenous and endogenous excitations. It is an "alarm signal" set off by the ego for two purposes: to prevent the situation from becoming traumatic again and to permit useful defense measures to be taken in time.

In final analysis, anxiety has a prophylactic function: that of preventing traumatization. This well illustrates the teleological character of Freud's doctrine.

These are the conclusions resulting from one man's initial searchings into the obscure depths of the human soul and the earliest manifestations of affectivity; and although they are liable to various objections, they possess the great merit of opening the door to further investigations.

Reflecting on Freud's profound formulations and trying to apply them to the treatment of cases of anxiety neurosis, I began to ask myself several questions.

Freud tells us that the core of the problem is danger. But for the small child to conceive of danger as such, one condition is necessary—he must have acquired the notion, the *subjective* concept of danger. Does this acquisition take place as early as Freud thought?

How, why, and when, does the child acquire the idea of "danger"? What is its genetic development and, particularly, what is the exact relation of this development to the formation of consciousness of the self? To answer these questions, the use of genetic psychology seems to me to be indispensable for it has at its disposition an experimental equipment that the practicing analysts lack.

Freud assured us that the very early production of anxiety is determined by the birth experience. But at that moment, the anxiety must be due to some chemical changes in the blood for it could not be the result of the combination of a danger idea tied to a memory of a previous traumatic situation. Asphyxia and memory are incompatible with each other. Considering anxiety a mixed phenomenon, that is, psychophysical, leads to ambiguity. However, to view it as determined always and everywhere by physiological factors alone blinds one to the psychological problems it creates in emotional illnesses. It would be impertinent today to refute the existence of these problems and their great importance in psychotherapy. Since the time of his paper, Freud founded his theory of neurosis on the very fact of anxiety as a pathological process. For this reason, a further investigation of the genetic development of anxiety is legitimate and essential to resolve the two problems necessary for the understanding and cure of these illnesses. The efforts of Freud call for new efforts on the part of modern investigators.

Freud has presented as an axiom the specificity of the danger situation in the creation of anxiety. On this point, common sense concurs and his most bitter opponents admit that he is right. Facing a mortal danger, most human beings are seized by fear which, in about half of them, develops into anxiety. Why this inadequate response of anxiety which inhibits judgment and action is absent in the other half is difficult to say. Be that as it may, the Freudian axiom can be summarized in these terms: the awareness of danger is the essential condition necessary for the creation of anxiety. However, reflection and numerous clinical investigations have led me to a different hypothesis.

It was the analysis of an obvious clinical fact that induced me to modify this genetic theory. This fact was an affective disturbance which occurred in many of my patients, and from which too many children suffer. This is the primary infantile phobia which appears in certain infants as early as the twentieth month and is capable of markedly influencing their nascent characters and seriously jeopardizing their future development.

The question is: can the concept of danger really play such a decisive role at so early an age? To admit this is to admit as a fact that at the age of twenty months the child's consciousness has already acquired the half-conceptual, half-instinctive idea of danger. To doubt it would necessitate a search for another anxiety-producing factor of a different order capable of replacing the one proposed by Freud.

One can start from the following principle. The feeling of anxiety, which breaks out in the face of a danger subjectively recognized as such by the subject, has already occurred in an earlier situation—akin, no doubt, to the danger situation but nevertheless preceding it. In the child it is then necessary to be very sure that the danger situation is compatible with the age and mental structure of the infant, that its description and objective analysis are applicable to the infant's emotional state and ability to experience: in a word, applicable to the actual contents of the infant's consciousness, be they ever so confused.

Every age and developmental stage of the child and of the adult has its own specific types of danger situations; each of these types implies a different state of consciousness and different subjective interpretations, some of which contradict each other during the progressive evolution of the individual. The great difficulty will always be to distinguish between the phenomena of consciousness as they unfold in the child, and the reality of their objects, that is, the agreement that may or may not exist between the subjective phenomena and the objective interpretations that we give to them. The feeling of danger which, according to Freud, the infant is supposed to experience, could be the result of an objective interpretation of the scholar rather than an exact translation of the small child's subjective feelings. Similarly, at birth it is not the fetus who declares himself in danger; the obstetricians state it—and Rank with them. We must not project our own concepts into the child's consciousness; he could accuse us of being unable to distinguish between what is ours and what is his, of being adualistic!

Conclusion. If the earliest anxiety-producing element is not danger or the internal perception of danger, what is it?

Our thesis is as follows: It is evident that the infant does feel something. His confused sensations make themselves felt as an uneasiness which develops into visible suffering. Noting the symptoms by which this suffering manifests itself, we infer that a particular affect has been produced, which we call anxiety. From this observation we can make a deduction. From a given point in development, during the second year, this affect indicates that a particular state has become differentiated: the state of subjective insecurity. The definition of this state is clear and simple. It does not at all mean that the child is conscious of having fallen into such a state as the adult conceives it to be. The child is able to react to these states of uneasiness without having acquired any concept of them. Conditioned reflexes take the place of thought, and we must not forget that we are describing a stage prior to language formation. In brief, the original element of anxiety is not danger but the state of insecurity. This concept seems best suited to the clinical facts.

This theory finds clear confirmation in the analytic investigation of adult as well as childhood phobias. In adults and children, phobias are so similar that they can be considered one entity. They are identical in nature and mechanisms, differing only in their secondary elaborations. With both adults and children, the feeling of insecurity is at the core of the symptom. The insecurity can produce a most overwhelming anxiety in the absence of any actual or objective danger. Then the feeling of insecurity alone determines the syndrome. The following chapters are an attempt to demonstrate these facts.

It is needless to add that originally the cause of the insecurity in the infant is, above all else, the absence of the mother (or her substitute) or separation from her at the time when the infant most needs her care and protection. This is the basic theory of anxiety as it relates to insecurity.

12. FREUD'S CONSTANT

Two kinds of anxiety-producing trauma must be considered:
1. physical accidents that endanger life (accidents, illnesses, poverty, and actual abandonment);
2. psychological accidents.

Scrutinizing every aspect of an individual's past, we do not always discover significant physical trauma, but we always find psychological trauma.[5] In a state of danger, it is easy to confuse psychic impotence with biological impotence; yet both remain very different processes. Certainly on the biological level, painful excitations due to tension arising from the nonsatisfaction of vital needs are perceived as such; but the discomfort created by these excitations cannot be identified with psychogenic anxiety. Anxiety is related to "the memory of a lived traumatic situation." This implies that the subjective value of a phenomenon by far exceeds the objective value. Even if a constant physiological

---

[5] I do not believe it is necessary to refer again to the theory of the "birth trauma" as a universal or primary factor. It is a superfluous hypothesis because it is unverifiable. However, the meaning of the so-called "birth dreams" deserves comment. These dreams of narrow and suffocating passages recur frequently in states of anxiety. In recalling attacks of asthma, whooping cough, or angina pectoris, patients will say, "It is like being in a vise." One can guess with certainty that these impressions have registered themselves in a "birth dream." One thing is true, the anxious person has a natural tendency to translate his subjective impressions into the concrete representation, the thorax.

basis can be found in psychogenic anxiety, it is the psychic element that is predominant and determining. For example, if a patient takes as an accomplished catastrophe that which is only a threat, or fears a purely imaginary danger, his feeling of helplessness is nonetheless overwhelming; in fact, it is greater and more overwhelming than the powerlessness of a normal subject exposed to an actual serious danger. This illogical intensity characterizes phobias and nightmares. (See case of Lucie, p. 69.)

Thus the recurrence of a painful memory of a past traumatic event makes the present happening seem traumatic, even though objectively it is not dangerous, or hardly so, to a nonsensitized person. We can easily verify this proposition. Freud based his whole approach on the idea of "unconscious memory" and later made it a part of the basic principle of unconscious psychic motivation. As we know, this principle has been attacked from various sides. However, a sound argument can be advanced in its favor: the remarkable uniformity throughout human life of the psychic motivations of anxiety. From childhood to old age, these motivations can be summarized in a word: the feeling of helplessness arising from insecurity. This is the constant core of the anxiety experience. The permanence of these anxiety-producing factors is a remarkable fact—as soon as they exist, anxiety appears. Thus the famous functional triad is—danger, helplessness with insecurity, and a memory of a past disaster. In a sense, life depends on the balance between misfortunes and their abolition, between past and present, memory and fact.

On the other hand, it is true that the motivations given by patients for their anxiety attacks vary as infinitely as external causes and internal conditions vary. In the adult, anxiety attacks often depend on adverse circumstances, unexpected complications, and sudden dangers. At least, the subject relates his discomfort to such things. He tends to see the source of his anxiety in exogenous, not endogenous factors. This work of exteriorization is facilitated by the many causes of anxiousness which exist in our times.

With most patients, there is no clear memory of the original trauma; however, its troublesome consequences automatically recur again and again. The subject remains unaware of these as recurrences since the relation between the primary trauma and the secondary ones is lost to memory. The therapist must re-establish this memory by tying together the links of the long chain reaching back to childhood. The regression goes back to the infantile level of magic thinking where malevolent beings threatened life and had the power to destroy it, as fantasied by the child in nightmares and phobias.

These beliefs undergo secondary elaborations in the course of the development of the affective life. Evolving from their primitive nature, they change their objects. It is no longer life itself but security that is threatened by evil powers: security that could be abolished by them at will.

Insecurity generates anxiety and conversely when anxiety becomes intolerable, it generates more insecurity. The level of tolerance for anxiety depends on the past as well as on the affective constitution, and varies greatly from one individual to another. Needless to say the tolerance is lower in predisposed subjects. However, Freud's triad must be completed by a fourth factor.

Insecurity-anxiety, the functional unit, does not belong to childhood alone but to the human condition. It exists at all ages; and whenever it appears, it provokes a regression of both thought and affectivity to the magic level.

Such a tendency to magic activity has nothing to do with intelligence per se, or with its evolution. Unintelligent as well as intelligent, educated people can be superstitious. Anxiety is not related to intelligence. In principle, all mixed areas of mental activity can be permeated by the influence of magic thinking. By the term, mixed areas, we mean those areas where the affects are habitually mixed or combined with the intellectual functions, as in love and social relationships. In some people, the areas of magic thinking are "protected" by carefully erected defenses; however, their immunity is precarious and they always remain vulnerable to anxiety; when anxiety occurs, rationality and logic disappear. Thus occasionally one sees the highly intellectual man or the very learned woman "get off the track."

In the last analysis, Freud's "constant" is nothing but the constancy of anxiety, its permanence throughout life in nature, form, and condition. This "constant" contributes a convincing proof of Freud's hypotheses. His patients' suffering opened new perspectives into hitherto unsuspected mechanisms of basic human nature.

Summary. Anxiety plus an acute feeling of helplessness plus magic thinking are characteristic of the infantile state which we find reproduced at all ages in all its particular conditions and specific elements. These are the fundamental elements of primary anxiety.

13. Littré's Definition[6] and L. Bovet's Concepts

In his excellent inaugural lecture, L. Bovet expressed himself in these striking terms: "If the future is the father of anxiety, the past is its nurse."[7] He alluded to the uncertain and threatening future. "We hope to have shown that the uncertain future is the very basis of anxiety. But from where do we get this gloomy notion of an uncertain and painful future? Evidently from our *past* ... Our memories of lived feelings of inadequacies, failures, rejections, and powerlessness govern our appreciation of

---

6 Littré, *Standard French Dictionary.*
7 Lecture before the Faculty of Medicine of Lausanne, June 12, 1942, published in *Revue Médicale de la Suisse romande,* Vol. 63, 1943, p. 17.

future dangers. These are the memories which we use when trying to stake out the future . . . and they may be faithful or distorted, be related to trauma which actually occurred or which we only experienced subjectively . . . but that makes no difference. What is important in the production of anxiety is that we base our prognostications and hopes on the experiences of the past. Only when the conclusions we draw concerning the dangers threatening us are objectively true can we be said to suffer from *legitimate and normal* anxiety. An example would be that of the old Alpinist following the hazardous ascent of his son through his binoculars and witnessing the misstep and accident with utter powerlessness."[8]

Hence, a future pregnant with danger and a past filled with painful memories generate between them an uncertain and anxious present. This is the temporal or time theory of Bovet. He attributes the essential role to time. We see that his thinking remains close to that of Freud, a fact which Bovet recognized. But one question must be raised. Is there also normal or justified anxiety?

In the beginning of his lecture Bovet quoted and agreed with Littré for whom worry, anxiousness, and anxiety are three degrees of increasing intensity of the same emotion.[9] We readily concede that dictionaries directed chiefly to men of letters often fail to make clinical distinctions; but from a strictly medical viewpoint, it can be questioned whether the identification of these three states throws more light or more obscurity on the problem of anxiety. This may indeed be a question of semantic convention, but to progress we must replace an unclear convention with a precise concept. To my mind, rather than equate anxiety, anxiousness and worry, it is necessary to distinguish

[8] *Ibid.*, p. 12.
[9] *Ibid.*, p. 11.

sharply between them in order to indicate the radically different origin of anxiety. Two reasons speak in favor of this distinction:

1. Worry and anxiousness are normal reactions.[10] Normal individuals react with them to uncertainty and all kinds of threats and dangers. They are normal in the sense that, far from clouding and misleading consciousness, they stimulate it, inducing it to evaluate the course of the dangers, provoking the desire to remove them, and taking adequate measures to do so. They do not destroy the capacity to judge a dangerous situation objectively because they are not accompanied by a feeling of total powerlessness. The danger is not prematurely confounded with sure disaster.

Anxiety, however, is responsible for many psychological disturbances. One of these seems so essential to me that it cannot be emphasized too much. The characteristic of anxiety in connection with danger is a dissociative action which it exerts on consciousness. The mind remains fixed on a certain aspect of a situation over and above all others. It is as if consciousness, annihilated, were discarding any reassuring thought and were riveting itself blindly on this one special but anxiety-producing idea. This idea is the anticipated representation of an accomplished disaster. Fully absorbed in this magic belief, the anxiety-ridden individual confounds possible disaster with certain disaster.

I can agree with Bovet in his analysis of the important role of the uncertain future only up to this point. If I am not mistaken, an uncertain future is not the cause of anxiety but its condition. Its real source lies, not in an uncertainty, but in the certainty of disaster—a vital disaster—which can lead the individual to his doom.

[10] Translator's Note: Following Odier, we make a clear-cut distinction between the words "anxiety" and "anxiousness." In English and American psychiatry, there has been a tendency to give these two words the separate meanings as defined here, although confusion still exists because of the similarity of the words and popular usage.

That the old Alpinist seeing his son's life endangered experiences worry and anxiousness is quite normal. On the other hand, to anticipate his son's mortal fall before any mishap would be an abnormal reaction. The certainty of a disaster and its anticipation always go together. The close relationship of these two subjective phenomena is sufficient to define the origin of anxiety.

The dissociative action of anxiety is characterized by two main elements. The first is of a selective character; it manifests itself in the choice of the anxiety-producing aspect of the danger situation, in the fact of selecting this aspect rather than any other. The second is its obsessive character.[11] Anxiety which does not begin or end with an obsession is rare. However, it is useless to attempt to determine whether anxiety causes an obsession with an unavoidable disaster or the obsession causes the anxiety. Actually this causal relationship is reversible and the two possibilities can occur alternately in the same subject. Finally, it is in the phobia that obsession formation is evident; therefore, it is particularly able to throw the phobic subject into a state of the most overwhelming anxiety.

2. The obsessive belief in a certain disaster has an affective origin and nature. However, to be expressed at the level of thought, it must rest on some mental structure. The obsessive belief must be molded into an intellectual form; crystallized into an idea; or founded on a judgment, however "para-objective" it might be. The mental structure or form of thought which the obsessive belief utilizes is magic thinking.

The principle of the omnipotence of thought is evident here, but it is the omnipotence of fear not of desire.[12] It is the fear of our own misfortune, suffering, failure, ruin, sickness, cancer, or

[11] I omit the cases of "anxiety without an object" or without expressable psychic content. This form of pure or essential anxiety is a special psychopathological condition which deserves more attention and study.

[12] The unconscious desire for the death or misfortune of the person in serious danger may also play a role in certain typical forms of anxiety.

"loss of the love object." Unconsciously, all these misfortunes are synonymous with near or distant but always certain death.

The identification of possible or improbable disaster with certain disaster can only be achieved by magic thinking. Freud discovered the origins of magic thinking in studying the early childhood of his patients. Certainly this is an age most favorable to the formation of phobias, as has been emphasized by the analysts. However, Piaget and the genetic psychologists demonstrated that it is also the age at which magic thinking is at its height. We would not be doing justice to the genius of these two men if we regarded this as a mere coincidence.[13]

Summary. The phobic subject projects into real or imagined danger all sorts of barbaric intentions and homicidal purposes. The same lethal animism is at work in his dreams.

A. Anxiety exerts a dissociative action on consciousness.

B. Anxiety causes thinking to revert to its original magic level and regularly revives infantile animism.

C. For these two reasons, anxiety has the power to create a combined regression of thought and affectivity.

So far as I know, neither worry nor anxiousness exert these three disturbing actions. This is the new argument in favor of the hypothesis that worry and anxiousness are, on the whole, normal reactions to threatening situations.

Beside the element of the intensity and the quantity of phobic anxiety, the quality must be emphasized. It is common to consider phobias as "exaggerated fears," as intense fears. But phobias

13 Magic thinking plays the chief role in the primary and symbolic thinking of the secondary phobias (appearing later, approximately after the third or fourth year). Moreover, the functional tie between magic and symbolic forms of thought is so close that they could be considered two aspects of the same intellectual process characteristic of the small child. The child never indulges in symbolic play without personifying his toys or animals. In the earliest forms of symbolic thought, the symbol is not distinguished from the symbolized, according to the laws of adualism. The symbol is magically invested with all the attributes of the person or thing it symbolizes.

and fears are two entirely different processes. Phobias always imply a magic or animistic interpretation of some part of objective reality. Likewise anxiety has functional qualities that distinguish it completely from anxiousness. If one is not sure that anxiety is present, it is better to speak of strong or intense anxiousness. We must remember that in German there is only one word, *Angst,* to designate both fear and anxiety.

For dynamic understanding, it is important to fix the point where a phenomenon or reaction ceases to be adequate, to obey the laws of adaptation to reality. This is the point where it becomes dysteleological or "parabiotic," to use current terms.

Born in childhood, anxiety always tends to pull the subject back into childhood. Fortunately this is not the case with anxiousness or worry.

These brief remarks leave the value and originality of Bovet's lecture intact. My remarks can provide either the corollary or antithesis of Bovet's thesis. Thus, to have happiness and serenity in the present, oblivion of the past is necessary—and I could almost say, of the future as well. The striking feature of this inference is its general, human applicability. Too many people never speak of happiness except in the past or future tense— and only those who are somewhat sure of the future use the future tense.

14. The Search for a General Principle

Anxiety is a phenomenon that is physical and psychic in nature and can originate in three different physiological systems as well as in three different modes. It may originate:

1. in the body when a vital function is impaired (i.e., asphyxia, angina pectoris, etc.); this is somatogenic anxiety;

2. in the endocrine and vegetative system, i.e., by a sudden discharge of adrenaline into the blood stream (Cannon) or other unknown disturbances;

3. at the level of the cerebral cortex, i.e., following sensations or emotions affecting consciousness; this is psychogenic anxiety.

A fourth psychopathological form exists, seen in schizophrenia, certain deliria or hallucinatory episodes especially in delirium tremens.[14]

Whether the source of anxiety is in one or the other of these systems, sympathicogenic reflexes are produced in the body explaining the typical sensations accompanying it—the most frequent being a sensation of thoracic compression. The seat of these neurovegetative phenomena, as variable as they are puzzling, would be the mesencephalon. On these points, at least, there seems to be general agreement at present.

However, two essential facts must be considered. First, total and combined cooperation of the three sources cited is not necessary. The action of any one of them is sufficient for consciousness to experience anxiety and to be affected by it. Secondly and more essential: the fact that this system or that is operating is unimportant. There is only one kind of anxiety, not three. It is of little consequence that the source of anxiety be an impaired organ, the nervous system, or the mind. In all three cases, the effect or the subjective result of all these processes is identical.

Hence, so far as anxiety is concerned, the psychic apparatus is functionally equivalent to the other two anxiety-producing

[14] "Anxiety has become a central problem in neuroses and psychoses. It represents an instinctive knowledge of psychic and physical vulnerability . . . In schizophrenia . . . an endotoxic process confuses the distinction between kinesthetic and external sensations . . . The schizophrenic is subject to a host of memories which confusingly invade him, as well as to a host of undifferentiated and unretained sensations from the lower brain centers . . . The subconscious and the conscious irrupt at the same time and generate anxiety . . ." (H. Steck, Psychiatrie et biologie. *Schweiz. med. Wochschr.*, 1927).

This interesting concept leads to the supposition that the normal individual possesses protecting dams against the invasion of consciousness by phenomena of an undifferentiated type which can generate anxiety. This dam can be broken by damaging the vital centers at the base of the brain or, as Professor Steck says, by damaging the "matrix (the mother, the womb?) of the instincts."

systems. Certain neurologists and psychiatrists have denied that the psychic apparatus alone is able to create anxiety. However, the analysis of certain reactions seems to prove that the process is reversible.

In some cases the source of the anxiety lies in the organ systems, i.e., the nervous system.[15] In other cases (psychoneuroses), the source of anxiety lies in the psychic apparatus.

Certainly we observe different forms of psychogenically determined anxiety. One of these concerns us in this study: the magic concept of insecurity. Under its influence, the subject experiences an overwhelming feeling of helplessness in the face of threatening events or threatening individuals upon whom he is dependent and to whom he imputes, as if by magic, almost absolute power and unconditional prestige. Such power and prestige preclude logical analysis; together they make up what we can correctly call the "authority object." Confronted with such a magic individual, objective reasoning becomes blind and paralyzed, thus excluding the use of all objective measures which might cope with the threat.

Summary. In certain cases, the production of anxiety is related to the impairment of a vital or biological function. In other cases, its production is related to the impairment or inhibition of essential psychic functions, especially ego functions. By an essential psychic function, we mean a function whose normal exercise is necessary for maintaining equilibrium and the activity of the ego. Impairment of such an ego function will cause anxiety.

[15] Physiologists and biologists have questioned if the mesencephalon should be considered the one and only executive agent of anxiety. The problem has given rise to numerous ingenious experiments which, however, are not conclusive. The question does not concern this study since we are focusing directly only on psychic anxiety as it is found in neurotic illnesses and dating from early childhood.

15. ANXIETY AND PRELOGICAL THINKING

Biologists agree on the one point that there is *normal anxiety* which man experiences when in danger of death. In the proportion that this reaction stimulates adjusting defense mechanisms, it is normal and adequate. Animals react similarly. In humans, the reaction is accompanied by full consciousness. The subject evaluates the danger without magnifying or minimizing it, or without comparing it to a previous trauma; then he acts.

If the endangered man can conceive of adequate defense measures and put them into action, his presence of mind and enterprising spirit are sufficient proof that he has no anxiety. Even if at first filled with surprise, worry and anxiousness, he overcomes these emotions and acts.

So-called normal anxiety leads to efficient action, starts motor phenomena. In contrast, so-called pathological anxiety creates affective phenomena which oppose action and induce magic thinking. It impairs the mind instead of moving muscles. Thus is produced the well-known clouding of the sensory organs that should be more sensitive and acute in the face of danger.

The following axioms are fundamental:

Without anxiety, logical action is possible. With anxiety, logical action is impossible. Without anxiety, prelogical action is impossible or at least improbable. With anxiety, prelogical action is certain.

For example, a patient recalls the following memory. "While reading in bed one evening, I suddenly heard noises and shouting. 'Fire,' they cry, 'The house is burning!' But instead of rushing out—instinctively, without reflection, I *put out my light* and hid under the covers . . . I was young and very fearful."

As the light was an oil lamp, to extinguish it was indeed a symbolic act dictated by magic thinking. In the frightened mind of the young boy, a *prelogical connection* took place between the little flame in the lamp and the big flame of the fire, as if the extinction of one would necessarily extinguish the other. Between the two elements there was mutual identity, and the defense mechanism is obvious: to escape the feeling of powerlessness and insecurity and the little fire was easy to put out.

In a state of anxiety patients react in one of two ways. The first is a kind of magic logic: resorting to preventive or superstitious modes of prelogical thinking to avert danger or abolish its consequences. The second is a magic logic using a negative or unlucky mode. These patients show an extraordinary "miscarriage of instinct"—instead of minimizing the danger and negating its existence, their prelogical thinking enhances and aggravates its dangerous consequences.

The symptoms of anxiety, conscious or unconscious, physiological and psychological, have been the subject of innumerable studies. With all the complex etiological factors, Freud was correct in stressing the importance of the feeling of powerlessness.[16] However, this etiology is reversible. The feeling of powerlessness can create anxiety; on the other hand, anxiety occurring first can itself create this sense of powerlessness and greatly increase it. Usually a vicious circle is established.

Very often the feeling of powerlessness comes first, is primary. Having felt for so long belittled, "completely stupid," crushed, and utterly incompetent, the subject experiences anxiety. Without realizing it, he then goes on from such feelings to the magic conviction of being surrounded and threatened by hostile powers which he will never be able to master. In this volume, we are chiefly concerned with the etiology of the primary feeling of inadequacy, its development and organization in the ego. How-

---

[16] This feeling must not be confused with the feeling of exhaustion characteristic of the fatigued individuals and the neurasthenic, where the etiology is different.

ever, in certain anxiety neuroses the feeling of inadequacy is secondary to the anxiety and, in turn, intensifies it. At any rate, the results are the same whether the initial factor is anxiety or powerlessness—in either case, the interesting point is the emergence of magic thinking.

I have observed cases of marked inferiority complexes with no anxiety. The patients did not show true anxiety but were worried, doubtful, and depressed. Unwinding the chain of their life experiences, we almost always find the origin of the inferiority complex in anxiety phenomena of childhood, be they phobias, nightmares, or anxiety attacks of which the parents were not aware. In adulthood, the absence of anxiety is more apparent than real. It remains latent, and adversity promptly brings it to the fore; and sooner or later with increasing failures and disappointments, magic thinking occurs. In these cases the latent anxiety is a silent survival of the fears resulting from childhood traumas.

The obligatory correlate of powerlessness or helplessness is insecurity. The former aids in rendering the latter absolute (i.e., *a*security). Together these two feelings are sometimes the cause, and at other times, the effect of anxiety,[17] depending on the patient, the circumstances, and especially on the nature of the early traumas. In the small child, helplessness and insecurity are usually the causes of anxiety. This is normal for the child and it is normal for him to resort to magic thinking when confronted with danger. In the adult, such a refuge is an anomaly, a "mental regression" in which rational and conceptual thinking are relinquished for prelogical thinking.

In the adult, anxiety is the most important factor in the

[17] A predisposition to anxiety must be related to constitutional or neurovegetative disturbances, i.e., organic factors.

mechanism which causes the patient to revert to the atmosphere of childhood where the laws of infantile psychology come into play again.

16. The Syndrome of Ego Dysfunction

In predisposed subjects, the feelings of powerlessness and insecurity are so closely tied together that they form a dynamic unity which is inhibitory and tends to become permanent. The chronicity is typical. The powerlessness and insecurity can become inner attitudes leaving deep and distorting marks on the character. These become the outstanding personality features and are constantly expressed in negative reactions to any ordeal. These relationships are very clearly seen in the neuroses of abandonment and of inadequacy. They may lead to one of the most overwhelming symptoms of ego psychopathology: the loss of the feeling of self-value, or the conviction of such an irreparable loss, which amounts to the same clinically. In inferiority complexes, the self-devaluation is less marked and regular but nonetheless constant. If looked for, it will always be found.

Magic thinking can produce anxiety as well as result from it; which sequence occurs depends on the patient's past. The prolonged existence of magic thinking and anxiety sooner or later produce what I should like to call the *syndrome of ego dysfunction*. There are three characteristic and related symptoms: feelings of helplessness, of insecurity, and of self-devaluation. Self-esteem may be completely absent (i.e., *avalorization*). Although noted by other authors, this last symptom has not received enough attention. It reveals a serious disorder of ego structure and functioning.

In the normal person, powerlessness in the face of danger does not produce self-devaluation if the danger is an objective reality. Many normal men and especially some of the geniuses, when they were ignored, slandered, persecuted, or imprisoned, experienced an increase in self-esteem—at the very time their contemporaries were trying to negate their value or to ridicule them. In neuroses, on the contrary, the reverse is true: loss of power means loss of self-value. This can be considered a fully verified clinical axiom.

Here are examples of a series of typical vicious circles: By exaggerating one's difficulties, one increases the inability to overcome them. By complicating and distorting the actual elements of a conflict—especially the conflicts of rivalry and achievement—and in overloading them with mixed emotional reactions, one increases the inability to resolve them. When a negative attitude dictated by a conviction of inadequacy is immediately and habitually adopted, any task becomes more difficult.

In disturbing and decisive circumstances, an individual may suffer from inferiority feelings but hide them behind "flattering virtues" (modesty, apparent selflessness, etc.). Even though these virtues mask the subject's inferiority feelings, giving him an appearance of high moral standards, he will remain unable to tackle the problems that reality presses him to solve. To solve them would require a personal affirmation of rights equal to one's rivals. In critical circumstances, one's superiors do not stop to give lectures on objectivity and logic; and only one's rivals benefit by such inadequacies.

In these ways, failures multiply, an attitude of defeatism and finally the syndrome of ego dysfunction come into existence. Born of anxiety, the symptoms become a source of more anxiety which sets off magic thinking. What in the beginning were mere feelings of inadequacy which one tried to ward off have progressed to unshakeable beliefs. Going from one belief to another, the subject attributes to them the magical power of rendering him helpless and of destroying his self-esteem.

Whatever the onset, the cycle of reactions is always the same. The course of the illness is stereotyped. With successive failures, the illness prevents and reverses the normal activity of the ego functions which should govern every member of a social community. The normal ego functions have never been established or put into practice.

We can restate the normal functions of the ego: These consist in the establishment of internal security sufficient to allow the individual to acquire that degree of power and self-value to which he can reasonably aspire. With this condition present, the individual will eventually realize his potentialities, be able to do what is within his capacity, to be what he is, no more nor less.

However, when the dysfunctional syndrome of the ego exists, it prevents the individual from achieving any of these basic ego functions.

THE THREE STAGES OF SOCIAL ADJUSTMENT

There are three related conditions or stages necessary to produce a healthy evolution of the ego. First, the absence of neurotic disturbances and a healthy education are the essentials for the normal formation and exercise of ego functions. In turn, their normal exercise, well directed toward internal valorization, promotes the establishment of internal security. And in a third step, internal security is necessary for an essential progress in social adjustment. This progress consists in the healthy application of the basic principles which govern human relationships, affective as well as social. These principles are mutual respect, sharing, and cooperation on the one hand, and self-autonomy on the other. No individual will be able to respect the autonomy of others unless he has acquired it within himself. Any person who has not partly or completely acquired a sense of his own self-value will not or only incompletely value these principles. From this source stems his difficulty in understanding their meaning and nature, let alone putting them into practice.[18]

However, to render these principles effective presupposes the ability to think rationally and logically, as well as a healthy ability to shield thought and judgment from the egocentric demands of affectivity.

In brief, these are the principal stages of an individual's "socialization." Many individuals do not achieve this healthy evolution of the ego. They remain at a certain stage and regress easily to the preceding one. For the most part, such patients suffer from anxiety feelings of inferiority and inadequacy.

THE FACTOR WHICH INDUCES MAGIC THINKING IS ANXIETY

A certain degree of rational thinking is indispensable to the normal regulation of ego functions. The normal regulation implies the ability to put oneself in the position of others; this ability and rational thought form the basis of what Piaget has called the "logic of relationships." We will note later an opposite kind of logic called the "prelogic of affective relationships," an infantile logic containing many magic elements. Freud and Piaget related these magical operations to a way of thinking, but it is also necessary to relate them to a way of feeling, of hoping, or of fearing. Which of these two mental modes, thinking or feeling, is primary and determining? To ask the question is to answer it. We can now formulate one of our theses:

1. The *primum movens* of magic thinking, the factor most capable of stimulating its activity, is found in the early fears of the child, in his feelings of danger, insecurity, and helplessness. (See Section 13.)

[18] The importance of valuing these principles in order to use them and render them effective has led me, in another publication, to call them the primary values. (*Les deux sources conscientes et inconscientes de la vie morale*, 2nd ed., p. 255.)

2. These fears incite the terrorized subject to maintain magic thinking, both as a defense and as a prophylaxis when dangers and threats are absent. The latter is exactly what is done by superstitious people. These two axioms are verified daily by our adult patients. This means that magic thinking exerts two opposing actions, at times an action of destruction and at times an action of protection. This functional dualism will be elaborated in succeeding chapters.

LOSS OF THE EGO

This disorder, especially when there is an overwhelming of the ego functions, is marked by a body of symptoms which constitute the ego syndrome. The syndrome may be partial or complete. In the latter case, the patient may reach a state of panic or exhibit the phenomenon of depersonalization.[19] The patient thinks, because he feels it, that his personality has been annihilated. Indeed, he behaves as if he had lost his ego. Furthermore, it is in those very terms that he tries to describe his discomfort, thus defining his feeling of total self-devaluation.

In dreams, the loss of the ego is symbolized by death. The patient dreams of horrible scenes in which he is exposed to insults, persecutions, and the cruelest physical assaults, in a word, to mortal danger. He can easily escape by awakening; and paradoxically the death-dealing anxiety brings him back to life

---

[19] Depersonalization is also found in hysteria, depressions, schizophrenia, etc. This is meant to be only a comparison, not an identification, between these two processes since their pathogenesis is different, psychogenic in some cases and organic in others. In his *Textbook of Psychiatry,* Bleuler says, "I am not quite clear about depersonalization because the patients who can give good information are rare . . . However, when the patients cease to feel their own volitional impulses, it is probably due to the repression of inner feelings, the mechanism and cause of which still remain unclear to us" (p. 107). The fact that the patients who can describe their symptoms do not require hospitalization explains the scarcity of the phenomenon among patients in mental hospitals. Yet, this "repression of inner feelings" could, in the last analysis, mean the same as the simultaneous loss of feelings of security and self-value.

by ending the sleep. In this concrete dramatization, the psychic catastrophe is expressed by an equivalent physical catastrophe. As a rule, dream thinking entrusts the morbid and destructive role to some omnipotent person. This is a special form of externalism characteristic of dreams (see Section 22) which we will mention again when discussing nightmares. The destruction of the ego is confounded with destruction of the body; and nothing but such a confusion better describes the suffering of the patient with this psychopathological syndrome.

THE MAGIC POWER OF MALEVOLENT REPRESENTATIONS

The idea, or better the feeling-idea (the two concepts are one at the infantile level) is closely related to a body of representations which we shall call negative or malevolent. The terms describe their general function which is to present the mind with images of disasters and catastrophes. But they are not mere images, and I shall insist on this point because an imagined disaster becomes an accomplished disaster. The subject behaves as though the imagined misfortune had really happened or will soon happen with inexorable certainty. Be the catastrophe a fact or only a threat, the anxiety is as intense.

When there is this confusion between threat and accomplished fact, we can say that the mind participates in the morbid representations of some possible or actual events. To express it another way, these representations are characterized by a "coefficient of realization" which is very high and even absolute. The phenomenon is most evident in phobias (imagined, intense, and unshakeable fears) and in nightmares. The only difference between the two is that the phobia occurs while awake, the nightmare during sleep. Phobias are the nightmares of the awakened state and nightmares are phobic attacks occurring when the conscious faculties of the ego are asleep. These are the two main categories of malevolent representations.

A patient feels she can never leave her home; for her this is a stark question of life or death, of security or total nonsecurity. If she were to cross the street, she would surely be the victim of some fatal accident. Her inner representation of the danger is enough to consider it a certainty, and her voluntary seclusion is proof of how certain she considers the danger. An inescapable danger calls for an absolute security measure: agoraphobia.

Everyone knows more or less what the terms phobia and nightmare mean. We can see their psychological structure and understand that they are based on magic thinking. However, these processes are much too important not to be studied more closely.

Summary. There is a close functional bond between magic thinking and anxiety, be the anxiety manifest or latent. The mechanism characteristic of this malevolent magic thinking is defined by and operated through the choice of morbid and fatal representations which are primarily affective in nature and origin. This explains why they remain so strong despite the fact that they can be objectively and rationally denied.

Their common object can be summarized by one word: threat. The threat may have various contents, such as physical or moral danger, incapacity, defeat, abandonment, loneliness, etc., or punishment, expiation, humiliation, etc. The degree of the threat varies and different feelings and attitudes may be involved.

CHAPTER TWO

OBJECTIFICATION OF AFFECT IN PHOBIAS AND NIGHTMARES

17. PHOBIAS

The most acute form of the dysfunctional syndrome of the ego is the phobia. Phobias and superstitions are closely related. Superstitious people have phobias of various catastrophes which are always possible, ever imminent, but actually never occur. If these catastrophes would actually occur, there would, of course, be no question of a phobia. The more frequent objects of these phobias are: thunderstorms, thunder, lightning, earthquakes, severe accidents, etc. In some cases, normal and innocuous events, such as the full moon or other solar and lunar phenomena, have symbolic value. The same distinction applies to the choice of phobic objects: pointed objects such as pencils, knives, needles, syringes, or actually quite "inoffensive" objects such as loose buttons, door handles, rough surfaces, etc., are feared. Any evil or sickness—bacteria, venereal disease, and especially cancer—may be the phobic object.

Beside the category of inanimate objects, there are the living beings, and in between, we can put the "moving objects," such as vehicles, especially trains, automobiles, shooting stars, and drafts of air.

The living beings can be animals—bulls, cows, mice, snakes, spiders, toads, or anything that creeps or hides. The human beings are policemen, government officials, or anyone with a peculiar psychic quality (the evil eye) or physical abnormality

67

(strabismus, a big nose, or any body deformity). The anomaly is believed to bring bad luck. And we cannot forget the "hexer" and "spell-thrower."

The study of phobias requires both the analysis of the unconscious motives and of the symbolism of the phobogenic objects (psychoanalysis) and the analysis of the phenomena themselves (phenomenology). Only the latter will concern us here.

From the phenomenological viewpoint, the absolute clinical fact is that the proximity or, worse, contact with the phobogenic object generates intense anxiety. A combination of insecurity and the feeling of helplessness is brought to a maximum in the phobia. The patient is not always conscious of this; and especially when the anxiety becomes too intense, he will no longer be able to analyze his feelings.

It is easy to see that the phobogenic object is invested with all the attributes of a malevolent force. Furthermore, one soon discovers that behind the phobogenic object hides a concept, an idea, a vague intuition. The patient intuitively senses that the object, inoffensive in itself, gets its morbid power not from within itself but from somewhere else. All phobics betray their natural tendency to animism. Since Levy-Bruhl, we have known that animism is a feature of magic thinking in primitive peoples; and since Piaget, of the magic thinking in children.

Thus behind the perception of the phobogenic object lies the idea of a *Being*, hidden, undefined, but alive.

The object itself is but an instrument in the hands of the Being who plays with it and uses it to carry out its evil purposes. Since the destructive power emanates from this Being, it deserves the name of a "malevolent being."

This conclusion is verified by genetic analysis. For the child at certain times, everything is animated, and everything can be endowed with intentions. The child attributes to objects the faculty of will, action, and all the characteristics of a living thing conceived after the image of man. Of course, animals admirably fit into the child's anthropomorphism.

A CASE OF CAR PHOBIA

A patient, Lucy, has suffered from a car phobia for many years. One day she brings me the following dream: "A baby carriage in which there is a baby is run over by a big automobile. I am anxious—because I am there but I am also the baby. What does this mean?"

Associating to this scene and the idea of death, she goes back to childhood and recalls a striking memory. At the age of two years and two months, she had the following intensely disturbing experience:

"On the edge of the garden where I used to play, there was a little house which I thought was a big cage. One morning I suddenly heard roarings coming out of this cage [a garage]. I felt a horrible fear . . . I thought a ferocious animal was coming out to get me! [The sound of the motor was confused with the roarings of a living being with evil intentions.] Paralyzed with fear, incapable of escape, I began to scream . . . and I forget what happened next."

The genetic connection remains between the actual phobia and the anxiety-producing incident of childhood. Today as yesterday, the car remains or becomes again a malevolent being. Do not cars run over people, helpless and condemned before their omnipotence?

Her phobia had extended to all vehicles; it was independent of the real quality of the drivers, whom the patient called "crushers." It was the noise, the explosions of engines that frightened Lucy and made her run. Without animism, such a generalization and the dissociation of the driver from the car would remain unintelligible. From the nature of the phobia, one would have to assume that in Lucy's eyes all drivers are inexperienced and reckless, if not sadistic; yet she affirmed that such a thought had never entered her head.

Big, noisy cars retained the attributes of a big, roaring animal, a murderous animal; and the survival of this magic and animistic representation is the connection between the present neurosis and the infantile trauma. We must emphasize the point that the phobogenic object, elaborated in childhood, remained unchanged in both its animistic nature and destructive function.[1] Unconsciously, Lucy attributes to cars a consciousness and a will, just as the child attributes these qualities to all self-propelled objects.

Remarks on This Case and the Importance of the Element of Space

Lucy also obeys a conditioned reflex formed during adolescence. Whenever she sees or hears a car, she cries out involuntarily, "Be careful—a crusher!" For her, there is no safe driver, all are "crushers." Whenever the phobia operates, a driver is no longer a human being but a kind of public criminal—the driver's license becomes a license to kill. Does this mean that, in her eyes, the driver himself is the malevolent being and not the machine he operates? It may seem so, but this is only the result of her adult mode of expression.

There are two distinct mechanisms at work, one of a regressive and prelogical nature, the other of an adaptive and logical nature. In the first, the driver participates in the destroying machine and its original malevolent power. He is included in the magic circle. Driver and machine are a "dynamic unity." Mind and matter are not—and we are in the midst of infantile realism. However, a

[1] See the above-mentioned work by Piaget, the interesting chapter in infantile animism (p. 157) as well as his remarks on precausality (p. 370). "Precausality presupposes an undifferentiation between the psychic and the physical, so that the real cause of a phenomenon is never to be found in the 'how' of its physical realization but in the intention which lies at its origin. . . . The child begins by seeing intentions everywhere. The distinction between intentional actions and mechanical movements is not innate but actually presupposes quite well-developed attitudes of the minds" (p. 229).

second mechanism operates. The regression occurs only on one condition: the patient has to be outside the car. She must experience the impending danger from without, as a threatened pedestrian. If she is inside a car driven by a known or unknown driver, he becomes, *ipso facto*, a human being again; and the car is considered normally as a material engine which obeys the will of man. Mind and matter are now differentiated.

The motives for this double transformation are evident. Inside the car, our patient is not in a traumatic situation; or more exactly, she is not in the condition analogous to the infantile situation; on the contrary, it is annulled.

Outside the car, she is a terrorized child seeing a roaring monster, a "car-animal" pouncing upon her; and it is the child who cries, "Be careful, here comes a crusher!"

This involuntary cry starts a flight reflex. In fleeing, she tries to escape from the phobia and to cling to the first protector she meets, if possible her husband. The phobic area is a well-delineated area of perception. Inside this area, anticipation of a possible but highly improbable accident is transferred into the vision of a certain and even accomplished one. However, when comfortably placed in a car, she is subjectively back in the mature situation and behaves accordingly. She now feels complete security and real pleasure; and the pleasure derives from being sure that the monster has finally been overcome.

As soon as a human being (in the full sense of the term) controls the engine, she can have full confidence in him. He is anxious to avoid accidents, and the machine itself has become indifferent.

The Structure of the Symptom

In further clarifying the interpretation of this symptom, it is necessary to distinguish between the spatial or physical and the psychic character of the initial traumatic experience. The physical character is that the car was exterior to the little child who heard it roar while standing in the garden. The psychic character lies in her fear of this mysterious engine. The second depends on the first, not the reverse. To say that the engine is the cause of the fear is to apply a logical principle of explanation. Here the causal link is one of precausality.

The engine could be the cause of such panicky fear only because it was invested with malevolent power. The external perception is interpreted according to the laws of animism; and fear becomes anxiety. Thus no complete explanation of the phenomenon can be advanced without using the data furnished by Piaget's methods and research.

Note that the two initial spatial and psychic characters are also found in the actual phobogenic situation. Analysis of the adult symptom allows reconstruction of the initial trauma and emphasizes its conformity to the laws of precausality. And, contrariwise, these laws permit us to throw some light on the structure of the adult phobia. The symptom is traced to the infantile trauma, and then the trauma is reduced to a phobic symptom.

The patient describes this twofold action in the process of causality. On the conscious level, the causal connection is: "The moving car generates my fear." The precausal connection takes place in the unconscious where the infantile principle remained fixed long after the initial trauma had been repressed and forgotten. In therapy, this principle must be revealed and its morbid consequence explained to her so that the severed relation between the affective reaction to the "crusher" and the affective reaction to the monster with magic powers can be re-established. In disturbances of this kind, the feeling of utter helplessness is always in the foreground.

With this example, I hope to have shown how much can be achieved by the combined method of interpretation of such symptoms.

Spontaneous Verification

A patient with long-standing anxiety relates the following:

"It was before my analysis. I did not know that anxiety was a well-defined disturbance and I ignored the term. A friend once asked me, 'But what do you really experience?' I answered him, 'Well, it is just as if I were tied and gagged on a road and a car comes at me at full speed.'" This is an image as symptomatic as it is spontaneous.

One observes great variety in the individual choices of the malevolent object. But in each patient the choice tends to limit itself to a certain image in preference to others. This fixation depends mainly on past experiences and former traumas, very little on actual circumstances or chance. All possibilities exist from the atom bomb to cancer, from the dentist to the income tax collector. These are the secondary objects whose symbolism always connects them in some way to their original objects. The transition from symbol to object lies in the degree of intensity and concretization, not in the nature of the phenomenon; the process of formation remains constant. This process, at the very depth of human nature, is the universal need to think magically when faced with cosmic and social forces. It is a profoundly human defense mechanism.

A FREQUENT ORIGIN OF AGORAPHOBIA

A woman suffers discomfort, palpitations, and dizziness whenever she is on any street. Instantly, she is pervaded with anxiety and fear of sudden death. In her anxiety, she retreats into primary realism; she projects the physical causes of a possible (and, as such, sure) death onto the external world. Hence the secondary illusion. The street as the place where she experiences anxiety is no longer considered the simple witness of the anxiety but is conceived of as being the sole cause of it. Thus, this sudden attack of externalism provides the patient with an infallible and obvious remedy. If only she avoids the street, she will, or will believe herself to be, cured of her fear of sudden death. However, the price of the cure is a new symptom, agoraphobia. The therapist can cure the second only after curing the first. In all these cases, one regularly finds an old trauma. In some circumstances, a child has believed that a thing or person wanted to kill him. This belief is not the primary cause but the secondary effect of an acute state of insecurity related to a sense of helplessness. This causality is the same in an adult.

In the clinical picture of agoraphobia, one usually finds a person whom I call the "protector." The protector, male or female, is a chosen person whose presence is sufficient to ward off any danger and cause anxiety to disappear.[2] The protector is a typical benevolent person. In phobias of automobiles, the role of the omnipotent protector is often attributed to the traffic policeman.

CANCER PHOBIA

There is a directly proportionate relationship between the degree of internal insecurity and the choice of the malevolent object. If the object is harmless in itself, we can infer that the insecurity is slight. Examples of such phobic objects would be pencils, bits of paper, pins, broken mirrors, twigs, pebbles, or cracks in the sidewalk upon which one must avoid stepping.

If the phobic objects are moving or living beings, the insecurity is more severe. In the cancer phobia, the insecurity is very strong, even fatal, springing from an almost total helplessness. The patient believes cancer to be incurable and this is the reason why he is obsessed with the idea. He chooses this object simply because of the impotency of medicine. The step from there to the

[2] Very often the protector is a rival, e.g., a dangerous enemy. The phobia is then an excellent way of controlling him! Its function is to appease jealousy.

belief of having cancer is very short and easily made by magic thinking. Unfortunately, cancer is a very real malevolent symbol.

In the fantasies and dreams of patients with cancer phobia, the cancer is externalized and takes on the aspect of something independent of the body, something that is animal, man or an apocalyptic mixture of both.[3] This thing with all the attributes of a malevolent magician is a quite well-defined evil personage. Through evil and lethal influences, he mutilates and kills his victim from the outside. The fundamental psychology of the phobia is once more verified: the patient projects onto the external world, attributing consciousness and will power to his imagined disease. This tendency to externalization is manifested in the realm of thinking as well as in the fantasies of these patients. A special mode of thinking occurs which is apparently rational, but is actually the product of magical projection.

Most of my patients were fanatic believers in the idea that cancer is caused by bacteria. They were absolutely sure that cancer is transmitted by another patient and that every person with cancer is a carrier of the dreadful germ. Such a person is ready to transmit the disease simply because he exists and is sick, which two characteristics make him a malevolent person. He exists, so to speak, with only one purpose: to contaminate. Furthermore, since many people may carry the disease undiagnosed, the conclusion is reached that anyone met at random may be infectious. Doubt becomes belief by virtue of magic thinking.

The same process operates in the more frequent but less well-differentiated phobia of any bacteria: the "germ phobia."

THE INEFFICIENCY OF LOGICAL PSYCHOTHERAPY

These "unshakable doubts" present a strong resistance to therapy. Only rarely is the internist or radiologist able to convince the patient after a thorough examination that no physical illness

---

3 *Cancer* is a Latin word, meaning crab or chancre.

exists and that he may rest in peace. The patient will counter with, "But, Doctor, how can you be sure, knowing the ignorance of science . . . one never really knows. . . . You say I am being superstitious but aren't you even more superstitious than I."

It is vain to "reason" with these patients. Magic can be fought only with another magic—with equal weapons. This is a law inherent in the phobic's psychology and accounts for the inefficiency of rational methods. The medical charlatans have drawn the logical conclusion here.

These patients must be analyzed to discover the cause of the regression. The greatest chance for success lies in attacking the process of regression itself rather than the secondary consequences. Piaget, who never pretended to be a psychotherapist, nonetheless saw that "a belief related to a special mental structure resists suggestion." Every physician treating patients with phobias and anxiety neuroses should remember this observation made by a psychologist studying children. Before attacking the adult beliefs, all the elements of the infantile structure which produced them must be analyzed.

One must first treat the underlying pathological structure. The therapeutic goal seems to me to be accessible only by the combined method utilizing the works of Freud and Piaget.

THE PRELOGIC OF THE PHOBIC PATIENT

As soon as the phobic patient believes that he breathes an atmosphere laden with deadly germs, he transforms his milieu into a malevolent environment. Starting with this absolute belief, he initiates action, that is, mechanisms of defense. These are of two types:

1. Preventive measures: he avoids all contacts, both through touching or the other senses. For instance, he may eliminate from his field of vision every possible or actual cancerous person. This imperious necessity leads straight to the "delusion of touching."

2. Curative measures: minute cleansings, rigorous measures of disinfecting. This produces the washing ceremonies; and such patients may spend all their free time in these ablutions.

Thus the secondary mechanisms may finally become the entire symptomatology. Actually it is quite logical for these patients to resort to these mechanisms; or at least it is an attempt to introduce a certain logic into a fundamentally illogical morbid process, to establish an appearance of rational order in the midst of irrationality.

A patient states: "If I leave my house and am alone on the street, I am so scared that I'm afraid I might do something absurd. I know I could lose my head and in order to avoid two trucks, I'd jump right in between them. Consequently, I have to be accompanied by a sensible person who will be able to protect me against all dangers, to save my life."

However, this patient can be sure of the protection of her protector only if she is sure of his kindness, his affection, and, if possible, his love for her. Thus her apparently rational logic is actually an "affective logic" inspired by fear. Rational and magic thinking are in principle contradictory. Nonetheless, even though they are logically mutually exclusive, they are not so in the presence of "phobic reasoning." In the minds of our patients, rational and magic thinking can be remarkably tolerant of each other and, in fact, help each other. To be more exact, if it becomes necessary, logical thinking is used to strengthen the conclusions reached by malevolent magic thinking. But is this true logical thinking?

A patient tells me, "This morning I disinfected myself from head to foot with alcohol. Yesterday evening I passed a woman in the street who had met a man whose postman has a wife who has just been operated on for cancer of the breast." (Letters and papers carry the "bacteria of cancer.")

Such an utterance is based on two entirely different principles.

1. The logical or scientific principle states that in the present state of medical science many modes of infection are unknown. Thus all suppositions are permitted; all precautions are legitimate, and the more the better.

2. The prelogical or prescientific principle dictates the above reasoning which is inspired by fear or by anxiety aroused by fear.

We are confronted here with a concept that I like to call an "idea-feeling" or an "ideo-affective representation" in order to emphasize its ambiguity. Anxiety prompted the patient to construct the whole chain of causes and effects going from the postman's wife to herself, in absolute contradiction to scientific knowledge. Every construction suggested by magic idea-feelings implies and reveals this kind of absolute egocentricity. In his analyses, Piaget always brought realism back to the essentially egocentric attitude of the child. Thus we deal only with prelogical reasoning in the phobic patient.

18. PRIMITIVE AND INFANTILE MODES OF OBJECTIVATION OF AFFECTS

FIRST STAGE: OBJECTIVATION OF FEAR

In some of his best papers, Piaget clearly outlined the genesis and characteristics of infantile prelogic. Therefore I will limit myself to recalling his three fundamental laws of prelogical thinking: the laws of precausality, participation, and magic implication.[4]

When a person with a cancer phobia wears a "magnetic belt," she herself as well as the quack who sold her the "antiphobic" object offer proof of infantile prelogical thinking. Both obey these three essential laws. If the quack is unbelieving and only out for money, he obeys still another law—but that is not our problem.

[4] *The Child's Conception of Physical Causality*, 1927.

The agoraphobic obeys the same laws and regresses in the same way when he invests his protector with the authority and power to abolish completely all dangers, physical and moral, which could threaten, no matter where he is or what he does. To transform a human being into a benevolent superman capable of protecting you from any malevolent being, and conversely, to turn a phobogenic object into a malevolent being is to return to infantile affective prelogic. It is not by chance that this occurs in so many adult neurotics; and the process is always related to the magic concept of security.

Phobia and the Projection of the Reciprocal or the Complement of Affects[5]

Again, it was Piaget who noted the essential psychological mechanism of the phobia, but the analysts seem to have ignored his observations. "It is difficult to distinguish from projection those instances when we attribute to other things, not our own characteristics, but *the complement* of our states of consciousness. Thus a child who is afraid of fire will attribute threatening intentions to it, not his fear. The fear is objectified, and the child projects into the fire the complement of his fear: wickedness."[6]

With such a mechanism, we are in the midst of infantile psychology, a whole primitive world of ideas and feelings which every psychiatrist should know.

Parents know that the child tends to divide people and things into two categories: his friends and his enemies, those he likes and those he dislikes, and reciprocally, those who like him and those who do not. Where dolls and animals are concerned, this division is very clear-cut. There are the good animals, but also unfortunately, there are many more bad animals. Objects that are not so classified are of no interest to the child; they are indif-

[5] See Introduction, p. 9.
[6] *La représentation du monde chez l'enfant*, p. 5.

ferent so long as affectivity does not differentiate them, so long as they have not assumed an affective value, negative or positive, in the child's eyes. His behavior toward them is animistic. He believes that animals know about his needs, wishes, and fears. These beliefs are the source of animal phobias.

In brief, the child's first conception of the world is that he is perpetually the object of the benevolent or malevolent actions and thoughts of others. The superstitious adult has remained at this stage.

The child feels much more freedom with objects and animals than with grownups and educators. With the former, he freely indulges his need for this "affective classification," easily expressing his wishes and fears, deceptions and demands, and particularly his grievances. From the concrete world, he borrows his animals and toys and through them expresses his impulsive affectivity. Toward parents, however, he feels no such ease. So many of our patients never dared to say anything during their childhoods; they had to "swallow" everything. Nonetheless they yielded to the need to classify grownups as well as dolls and animals into good and bad people—even though this activity went unnoticed by many parents and genetic psychologists. The therapist discovers the origin of this tendency which is still manifest[7] and logically deduces that it has simply persisted since child-

[7] This tendency may take the following form, especially in women. A woman will yield instantaneously and without reflection to the "snap" judgment that another person, especially another woman, is "sympathetic" or "unsympathetic." The decision is made at once and thus precludes a value judgment. There is no middle road. Any woman not belonging to one or the other category is completely indifferent; she just does not exist. For to exist, another person must evoke either a positive or negative reaction. This strict condition is the result of a belated infantile mechanism.

The motives behind these spontaneous judgments and peremptory choices are numerous, and can be real or symbolic. "As soon as another woman wears stockings with runs in them, I immediately like her." The therapist can foresee what is behind such a criterion. In general, every person toward whom one feels inferior is at once classified as unsympathetic and disliked. Because of a real or fantasied superiority, the other person devaluates the subject, and is

hood. The principle of this infantile tendency can be summarized in two propositions:

A. Whoever threatens and frightens me is wicked. Thus I do not like him.

B. Whoever reassures and protects me is good. Thus I like him.

Proposition A expresses a negative conclusion which is natural enough. However, the antipathy and hate are not always expressed and very often remain repressed. At any rate, they are secondary to the fear.

In children, these negative reactions are expressed in spontaneous reactions such as the following. A baby bangs himself against a table. Two reactions follow corresponding to two successive stages. In the first stage, the child feels pain, is stricken with emotion and begins to moan and cry. This is chiefly a physiological reaction. Absorbed in pain, he ignores the table which assumes no particular significance to him. Then a psychological reaction is superimposed on the physiological one. The baby now fears this table which has hurt him. He now avoids it as he avoids the fire that burned him. In putting space between the table and himself, he resorts to an elementary defense reflex. Such a minor phobic attack may later be extended to all tables and all pieces of furniture.

Mutatis mutandis, the adult with phobias adopts the same negative reactions toward his phobogenic object, as if he had remained subjected to the primary reflexes of children and primitive peoples. Indeed the object is malevolent only if it comes into physical contact with the body, which is why one must not touch it or be touched by it. Visual and auditory contact are threaten-

---

therefore threatening and dangerous; and the patient will consider her wicked and will attribute hostile feelings to her. Thence the thoughtless and impulsive antipathy toward this producer of trouble, conflicts and unhappiness and the need to take refuge with a congenial being who raises no such problems.

ing but not yet malevolent. To see a person with cancer is alarming; to touch him is deadly.

SECOND STAGE: OBJECTIFICATION OF ANGER

In the second stage, things are more complicated. Through his reaction to the table, the child shows us that he has acquired a certain idea about the world, related to the acquisition of a certain mental structure.[8] He is not now, or only briefly, a prey to his emotions; instead he reacts to this hostile world, which he knows to be external to himself, and he acts. He hits the table "because it is bad" and he wants to punish it. He strikes back. This is no longer reflex but is a psychological reaction ruled by the laws of affective prelogic. Parenthetically, any object or person who resists the child is *ipso facto* declared "bad" and classed in the malevolent world.

Mutatis mutandis, with more refined and complex motives, the "persecuted" adult reacts in the same way.

Summary. There are two reactions:

A. Before the bad fire, the child objectifies his fears.

B. Before the table, he objectifies his anger.

Both reactions may persist until one finally predominates over the other. This predominance will influence and shape the character. In adult psychopathology, both objectification of fear and objectification of anger characterize certain forms of neuroses, manifesting themselves in excessive and exaggerated ways.

19. MENTAL STRUCTURE AND THE STRUCTURIZATION OF REALITY

A child inclined to fear reality is disturbed when he discovers evil elements in a world which up to that time had been only

---

[8] As soon as the child acquires a certain mental structure, he attributes a corresponding structure to reality. He "structures" the world in the image of himself.

tender, smiling, and benevolent (the theme of "Paradise Lost"). And regularly, his unsuspected enemies strike him hardest and most frequently when he least expects it.

All this occurs in the critical stage aptly illustrated by "the fear of the bad fire." I would like to call it the stage of "primary anxiety." The specific mechanism here is that of the "projection of the complement." Thus we see that our patients regress to a very early stage of development in their phobic attacks.[9]

On this level the patient feels and acts as a victim only. Secure and self-valuing attitudes are no longer available to him. His only defense consists in avoiding every contact with all malevolent elements and in suppressing them from the external field of perception. Such a motor mechanism has its psychic equivalent: repression. Repression is then the suppression of all anxiety-producing factors in the internal field of perception— their elimination from consciousness.

Thus all the essential characteristics of the stage of primary anxiety are found in phobias. The phobic patient is a child who

---

[9] To me, this stage seems to correspond to Freud's stage of "primary masochism." His term would define the instinctual component of this early stage, and the term of "projection of the complement" defines its psychological component. In my mind, the very intricate problem of psychic masochism is dominated by the phenomenon of primary anxiety.

Since Freud, analysts have considered phobias to be the least regressed form of neurosis, which, like hysteria, stops at the genital and oedipal stage (fourth-sixth years). In my opinion, this is not true for the clear-cut phobias characterized by the above-described processes. The regression does not stop at the oedipal stage but goes far beyond it, as deep as regression can go. The etiological factor is not an oedipal conflict but a much more fundamental one. The effect of the earliest traumas sustained when the child faces reality is a stark polarization of two absolutely contradictory tendencies: the being-able-to-live and the not-being-able-to-live. This antithesis is often better expressed as the will-to-live and the absence-of-the-will-to-live.

This latter tendency becomes fully realized in the phobic area. When a subject ascribes malevolent powers to an object, the effect, among others, is to render the subject blind. He can no longer see what is visible to everyone else, that he is his own sole tormentor. He is completely unaware of his masochism which is unconscious because it has preserved its infantile, realistic mode of expression. Cancer, for example, is viewed as external to the mind that conceived it and believed to be due to an imaginary germ.

still believes in the murderous wishes of things and people who make him suffer or who resist him. And his only defense is an infantile, magic one.

In the phobic area of the adult patient, this structure has remained unchanged. On the one hand, there is a magic and pre-logical mental structure; on the other, there is a similar structuralization of reality. The latter necessarily complements the first. The patient with a phobia remains at the stage of the "fear-of-the-bad-fire."

This deep regression in phobias is identical to that in the nightmare which, from this point of view, may be considered as a nocturnal attack of a phobia.

In later stages, the subject refuses to admit defeat. He refuses to be the victim any longer. Retaliating, he hits that which hit him. This is the stage of the "table-who-hurt."

This development means that an important modification of the mental structure has taken place, as well as a corresponding restructurization of reality. If life is endangered, one not only can defend oneself, one must. The abuses of reality are no longer absolute; they can be corrected and their dangers are relative to the reactions of the subject; or better, now their victim's reactions make them relative. In this second stage, the subject no longer hesitates to use his own aggressiveness to defend himself against the aggressiveness of the world. This then is a reactive aggressive pattern. In this sense, aggression is not an action, per se, but a reaction. Its chief motive is not the pleasure of hurting but the necessity of paying back, an impulsive defense mechanism.

Indeed, what started the sequence of events: the child or the table? The phobic patient or the cancer? Lucy or the car-animal? To this question, the three victims are unanimous and categorical in their answers.

In the phobic neuroses, regression reaches the lowest level; however, in the neurosis of abandonment, it stops at the second stage of reactive aggression. In these patients, the same tendency to benevolent and malevolent investments exists, but there is an essential difference from the thinking of the phobic patient. Patients with neurosis of abandonment no longer attribute magic powers to objects or animals but only to humans. A well-known, familiar person with special features will possess and exert magic powers. Hence benevolent and malevolent qualities are always personified. This very interesting disorder will be discussed in detail later.

Identification with the Persecutor

To be complete, a third stage must be described, or better, a more highly developed type of reaction.

Lucette, age six, suffers from a severe phobia of barking dogs. All educational and therapeutic measures have been to no avail. One day her mother hears strange noises from the garden and ran out to find her daughter on all fours "barking furiously."

Lucette has found her own treatment. By becoming one of the dogs, she appeases them and makes friends with them. Hence she no longer fears these frightening animals. To put it another way, the roles were reversed; instead of experiencing fear herself, she inspires fear in her own little playmates and imposes upon them the unpleasant fright which she now disowns. And she cured herself of her phobia.

This is the very curative process of identification with the persecutor[10] and it plays an important role in other types of neuroses. It is a more complex and evolved form of objectification and presents problems outside the scope of this work. I simply mention this phenomenon of the incorporation into the ego of the attributes of the wicked.

However, traces of this phenomenon can be seen indirectly in

[10] The mechanism which Anna Freud described as "identification with the aggressor" (*The Ego and the Mechanisms of Defense*. New York: International Universities Press, 1946). (Trans.)

the cancer phobia. Fearing cancer, or rather the hypothetical bacilli of it, one patient endlessly repeated, "I don't fear anything for myself—I'm only afraid for others." Such a calm statement presupposes an absolute personal immunity which is already suspect. Actually she fears she will contaminate others and hence considers her body infected with microbes and the focus of dissemination.

In this process are three movements:

1. Centripetal. She is infected with all the cancerous microbes in her environment. At this point, she is the victim of an offensive reality and of the inherent wickedness of her society.

2. Incorporation of this evil and identification with the malevolent being. Now she has become a public danger, a threat to others. As she puts it, she exists only to infect her neighbors and thus her innumerable magic preventive measures.

3. Centrifugal. In her imagination, she expands the plague and she may bring death to every person who comes near her, penetrating the malevolent zone surrounding her. She is, or believes herself to be, an evil-producing monster. In brief, she takes revenge for her unhappy childhood.

The Two Worlds

In most children, the fundamental tendency to separate reality into two opposite worlds, the good and the bad, is quite evident. In the person with phobias, this tendency reaches a maximum and retains its strong and categorical character.

The "phobic sector" is the area of anxiety. It is a kind of magic circle with the phobogenic object at its center; and the circle is well delimited when this object is well determined, visible or tangible.[11]

[11] The same applies to germ phobias. The phobic sector can be extended to all space because germs are invisible and present everywhere. The area of anxiety is then internally delimited; if the patient has the idea that germs are everywhere, then wherever the patient is, is a phobic area.

The phobogenic object concentrates in itself all the evil of this world and exerts all the cruelty of which animals and things are capable.[12] For the patient the object has a complete monopoly on sadism.

When in the grips of his phobia, the patient is haunted by the idea of death, an imminent and unavoidable death if he does not resort to his curative measures (flight, disinfection, etc.). There is no question here of an "easy death" or deliverance. What threatens the patient is a terrible and painful death that only a malevolent being could invent and inflict. I shall call this the "malevolent death."

Every adult knows that cancer is painful and deadly; and every child knows that fire burns badly and is lethal, just as it destroys everything it touches.

In the area of the phobia, the feelings of total powerlessness and insecurity reign, as well as a profound sense of self-devaluation. These feelings are indissolubly tied to the idea of death, of physical destruction.

The Vital Sector

The chief characteristic of the vital sector is the absence of anxiety. In order to reach this condition, the subject has to sever all ties with the phobogenic object, the instrument of his destruction. Free of anxiety, he first experiences a kind of mental and affective neutrality, then quickly transcends this rather negative state and experiences an ardent desire to live again and to be like others. Anxiety is tied to the idea of death; its absence to the idea of life. Patients often speak of their new state as of a resurrection.

---

[12] Interestingly, I have never observed phobias of plants. On the contrary, the world of plants seems invested with beneficial virtues. Let us recall the totem tree, protector of the tribe, and closer to us, the tree-planting ceremonies celebrating victory and peace. The joy of people relates to the idea of protection, of feeling secure, and of ushering in a "new era."

Once the malevolent dangers are lifted, the patient recovers his previous personality and attempts to fulfill it. He also recovers the normal use of his faculties and his common sense. The return of a sense of security re-establishes the capacity for adjustment to the environment. As soon as normal interpersonal relationships are possible, the patient has a strong desire to lead an affectively gratifying life.

The patient now believes himself cured and wants to prove it. He is at first surprised to be in possession of such remarkable strength and qualities—who, for instance, would have suspected them in a woman previously so afraid of mice, spiders, or toads!

Here we touch on the discrepancy between imagined fears and real fears. For the phobic patient, the imagined danger has much more reality than real danger. Many patients with phobias when faced with real, objective danger, will recover all their faculties, show initiative and great presence of mind. Their actions are now rational, not magic; logical, not prelogical. If a sense of insecurity is still present, it no longer paralyzes the subject who now fights it with adequate action.

For instance, Lucy shows remarkable courage when in danger; she is actually more courageous than the average normal person. However, for this courage to manifest itself, one absolute condition must be fulfilled: Lucy must be out of sight and reach of any "crashing" cars. This condition exists when she is on sea or climbing mountains. To her these are safe places where she can confront danger and death calmly; she experiences thunderstorms and tempests without the least anxiety. A paradox? No, only the rational behavior of a person of energetic temperament freed from her phobia and thus able to assert her true nature. Recall also that inside a car, she fears no accident—the thought does not even cross her mind.

One could conclude from this contrast that there exists a phenomenon of overadaptation to real danger as a compensation for the lack of adjustment to imaginary ones. Because of the feeling of total powerlessness, the latter becomes the more real of the two.

Like little Lucette mentioned before, another patient found an infallible remedy for his phobia of fires. He produced dreams in which he was a fireman, and his nightmares about fires were ended. This is the mechanism of identification with a benevolent individual in order to overcome the malevolent one. This mechanism has a social value which the opposite mechanism, identification with the malevolent being, lacks. I advised this patient to become a fireman, and since doing so, he has required no further treatment.

Another patient had a phobic fear of cows. He recovered after having passed his phobia onto his wife and then became her "therapist."

The Function of Love

Love is a second method of recovery, of restoring the feelings of security and valorization. No evil is more self-devaluating than a phobia in full force. When freed from anxiety, repair of the damage is demanded by the ego.

One of the first moves of such patients is to establish friendly and affectionate relationships with congenial people, and if possible, a love relationship. The re-establishment of feelings of security and self-value through love occurs most intensely in patients with neuroses of abandonment and with phobias. One condition must exist, however—the patient must be sure of the quality, sincerity, and permanency of the feelings he inspires in his love object. With the phobia gone, he tends to rely on a positive affective relationship for his security and emotional balance. He now very much wants to maintain excellent relations with everybody. The contrast between his present personality and that during the phobic attack is striking.

Sometimes he chooses as a love object the person who acted as his protector during the phobia. The better the protector fulfilled his role, the more the patient becomes attached to him; and this attachment easily turns into love. The more the patient loves his protector, the more he feels protected by him.

Love restores to the patient what the phobia had taken away. A positive love life is the best antidote to anxiety and insecurity. In giving security, the loved one becomes the benevolent antidote to the phobogenic object. Thus love abolishes the dysfunctional syndrome of the ego and re-establishes order in the ego functions so shattered by the previous crisis. This regularly occurs in the neurosis of abandonment.

The contrast between alternating periods of profound disturbance and healthy functioning ceases to be paradoxical when compared to the original situation in the frightened child. Every child has gone through painful experiences and has "lived" such contrasts. After burning himself on the stove or bumping his head on the furniture, the terrified child flees from these awful things to take refuge in his mother's arms. Tenderness dispels terror and the little one is brought back to life by the enveloping atmosphere of security. Mother creates an area of protection around her. She is a real magician, able to reconciliate the malevolent beings and their little victim. The fire no longer is bad, and the table no longer can hurt. Mother has "arranged everything."

Two Modes of Malevolent Investment

In certain phobic patients, mutual love produces calmness and happiness. However, such love can become dangerous in that the above-described relations between the phobia and love can be reversed.

Protection in itself is a powerful bond and a guarantee against the deep insecurity engendered by the phobia. Hence the affective relationship becomes most precious and must be preserved in all its strength and meaning. Yet the condition *sine qua non* for its preservation is the existence of the phobia. The phobia must remain if the love is to last. The phobia makes the love legitimate. The phobia obliges the protector to exercise more patience, show more kindness and put "more feeling" into his missionary task. The phobia assures the continuation of the love, and the love preserves the phobia, or at least, induces the patient to reactivate it in order to bring back an unfaithful protector.

Many children utilize a similar technique. The more they are afraid, the more love and attention they will receive.

Clinically, we often find a recrudescence of phobic attacks after disappointments in love. Often, the exacerbation of symptoms appears when the relationship with the protector has cooled with frequent quarrels and discord. In case of actual separation, i.e., "loss of the love object," the aggravation of the symptoms becomes quite acute. Not infrequently, the lover and protector becomes tired of the eccentricities of the one he protects. When this happens he throws the phobic patient back into the throes of anxiety. The loss of love is accompanied by the loss of security, this correlation manifesting itself in a reappearances of the phobia. Insecurity is expressed by the phobia and can, in severe crises, reach its peak—*a*security. On the other hand, I have seen a case of phobia spontaneously cured by a "great love."

The neurosis of abandonment and phobias have many features and symptoms in common. One of these is the care lavished upon affective relationships, often almost to the point of worship. In both, the positive affective bond is valued so highly by the patients because it spells security.

In both disorders, when loss of the love object occurs, the patients revert to a process of infantile magic investment. But from then on, they vary on one point. In the phobic patient, it is the phobogenic object which is invested with evil intent and malevolent attributes; in the neurosis of abandonment, the patient imputes these evil attributes to the love object who has betrayed him.

However, whether the patient imputes evil intent to a material object or to a human being, the process is the same. It is always a serious regression to the level of primary infantile anxiety. On this level, the process retains its early psychological meaning as an effort to objectify fear and, finally to objectify the rage inspired by a hostile and powerful reality. In the last analysis, these anxiety-ridden people seek to objectify the tremendous fear aroused in them by a sudden and total loss of the feeling of security.

This process of objectification can be realized only when the patient is in the waking state. The external reality must be visible and tangible if the patient is to project his fears onto it. What happens when he is asleep is a quite different matter. Nightmares seem logically inconceivable; yet they exist.

The Priority of Affect

Only because of his phobia does the patient divide the world into two categories. The division is not based on any ideas or conceptions of reality. The determining factor is not a concept but an affect. Observation of an anxious child's behavior leads to the same conclusion.

In processes of this kind, conceptual thinking does not create the affect or regulate its course and intensity. On the contrary, it is the affect which induces the subject to choose one concept rather than another. Thus anxiety induces the use of prelogical concepts and magic thinking. This would be the principle of the affect in neurotic behavior stressed by the analysts. Is this priority an outgrowth of the adult neurotic process or an inheritance from the psychology of childhood? To my knowledge, no genetic psychologist has yet published a work covering this whole question. The problem here concerns the functional relations and interactions between the affect and the concept in the child. It seems a most important problem to me, and further research in this direction would be of great interest to psychotherapists and educators. To the therapist treating adults, there is no doubt that affects rule over concepts.

Summary. Two principles concerning the regression of phobic patients to infantile realism can be stated:

1. Every phobogenic object, even the most inanimate, is endowed with malevolent intentions.

2. Hence, it is also endowed with magic omnipotence.

These are the essential elements of psychic regression in patients with phobias. Phobic thinking obeys the laws of magic thinking. This much can be verified even by a most superficial investigation of our patient's statements and reactions.

The phobia is produced entirely by the action of primary realism; it obeys all the laws of prelogical thinking and prelogical affectivity. Created in the imagination of the child, it inevitably appears first in childhood. The phobia, especially in the form of night terrors, is the typical neurosis of children.

20. A Genetic Analysis of Nightmares

I have attempted to delineate certain types of infantile affects of a destructive, almost an antibiological, character. If not dispelled, these intense emotions are fully discharged when they encounter conditions favorable to their release. Such a condition is found in sleep.

Nightmares owe their violent character to two phenomena:

1. The weakness of the ego during sleep. Sleep dissolves the

ego's protective mechanisms against the unconscious and its dynamisms (Freud's *Reizschutz*).

2. The fact that the objectifying mechanisms in the phobia lose their value and function in the absence of reality and conscious thinking. The space where objects are localized by the dreamer is as illusory as the objects themselves. Their image is a pure visual hallucination.

The hallucinatory nature of dreams raises difficult problems beyond the scope of this work. I will limit myself to certain considerations of the psychological modalities of dream thinking from the genetic viewpoint.

We have been told that the determining factors in nightmares are unconscious guilt feelings or the need for punishment, or even certain masochistic needs, eroticized and not admitted. If these psychoanalytic explanations are valid for certain painful dreams, they do not explain the true nightmare with its characteristic structure.

To my mind, every true nightmare represents a regression far beyond the above-mentioned superego-determined processes. The nightmare corresponds to a clearly recognizable regression to the stage of primary infantile anxiety. This regression accounts for the essential characteristics of this truly astonishing phenomenon. We will cease to be surprised only when we realize that the idea of death is at the basis of nightmares and dictates its drama and images.

Activated by anxiety, malevolent magic thinking creates the plot and produces the fatal ending. The sleeper takes the images suggested by this primitive thinking quite seriously; and the frightening situation is similar to the earliest phobic reactions of the small child. In fact, the nightmare, like the phobia, has the ability to realize all the consequences inherent in malevolent images.

A second feature common to both is the objectification of

fear. This feature of the nightmare seems paradoxical. How can one objectify anything in the absence of any objective reality? Does not the dreamer lack the material support offered to the phobic patient by the concrete world?

The answer to the paradox is that, in the phobic patient and the child, we deal with a real fact and a verifiable mechanism, while in the dreamer all we have is a belief. Nonetheless for the dreamer, the belief in the objectivity of the dream world and what takes place in it is absolute. Even more than ordinary dreams, the nightmare is based upon such subjective certainty. We might say that the "reality coefficient" of the nightmare is absolute. During the nightmare, the adult believes as much in the reality of the images created by his mind as the child believes in the evil power of fires.

A third common feature of phobias and nightmares is the systematic use of projection of the complement. In the phobic patient and the child, projection leaves in its wake an intimate affective relationship of a negative sort between the subject and the phobogenic object. The image of the phobogenic object becomes repulsive. The burned child fears fire (or any other offensive element of reality).[13]

[13] A father notices that the stove has become taboo for his daughter (two and a half years). The cause is obscure, but the phobia of the stove is clear-cut—and this is the only object in the apartment having anything to do with fire. The father has attempted some psychotherapy. Little Catherine is placed a good distance from the stove, and while she watches, her father smilingly and playfully touches the stove repeatedly. This first session fails and Catherine runs away frightened. The treatment continues the following days with the father even sitting on the stove with a happy expression. The child's anxiety gradually diminishes and is replaced by simple fear. Encouraged by this success, our "therapist" decides to use more drastic measures. The child must experience for herself the innocuousness of her phobogenic object. After touching the stove with his fingers, showing no pain, he approaches Catherine with the same fingers outstretched. He is sure that his attitude, so full of love, his smile and cheerfulness will reassure the little girl. However, he is disappointed; the child becomes panic-stricken and runs away sobbing. Her "doctor" has forgotten the phenomenon of magic contagion.

Thus the malevolent object, even if a material substance, is transmittable

Such an affective, prelogical relationship is due to fear and lasts as long as the fear does. In neutral areas, the phobogenic object loses most of its power; however, it never disappears completely. The tie is always there, conscious or preconscious, always and everywhere latent.

In the germ phobia and the phobia of cancer due to germs, the phobogenic object never loses its power because these malevolent agents are not fixed in space. The patient is always and everywhere pursued by them except in sleep, unless he has nightmares. If he tries hard to fight the phobia, nightmares will recur night after night. The fear accumulated during the day will be released in the nightmare. Hence in this type of phobia, space offers no protection. There is no "neutralizing space."

As a result, the defense mechanism used in the projection of the complement is bound to fail, at least partially. The appearance of an affective and magic participation following projection becomes both the agent and the witness of this failure. If the participation were to disappear, this mechanism would succeed. However, the absurdity of such a conclusion is evident. The participation is caused by fear and cannot disappear so long as its cause exists. And if the fear disappears, its projection is no longer possible.

In summary, in the usual phobias, projection is applied to a real object existing in space, is visible and of material form. Hence, it is relatively easy to avoid it and so escape its influence.

However, in the nightmare the rule of "completive attribute" is the same, but its point of application must be different because the malevolent object is an unreal object falsely localized in an

---

despite the immunity of the transmitting object (here, the fingers). "Father is not burned by the stove, but Catherine is!" This prelogical reasoning shows the phenomenon of affective participation to be a personal relationship between the subject and his phobogenic object. In this purely subjective relationship, no person or thing can intervene.

imaginary space. The neutralizing function of real space is non-existent. For the dreamer, projection is useless.

We must distinguish between two degrees of projection corresponding to the degree of influence exerted by the magic processes.[14]

1. Partial adualism. Reality as such still exists with all its characteristics and is modified only at one point. This selective modification is due to a selective projection. The phobic patient keeps his fear and projects only its "complement" or "reciprocal." With its confusion of internal and external, the adualism pertains only to that which is related to the phobogenic object.

2. Total adualism. Reality no longer exists and its characteristics are lost. Projection is total. This occurs in the nightmare.

When we dream, we do not know that we are thinking and dreaming.[15] We are completely ignorant of the mental processes that go on and are ultimately translated into dream images; the confusion is complete.

[14] Magic thinking is intimately related to projection. Without projection, it would be impossible because magic thinking attempts to influence the outer world and modify its reality by modifying its cosmic or social determinism. The magic process is, among other things, a real "syndrome of exteriorization," of which the dream is the purest and most imaginary example.

The magic process starts with projection; i.e., locating in the outside world that which occurs within the mind and localizing outside consciousness the subjective psychic relations.

In a second stage, the subject conceives of these subjective relationships as completely dependent on other people, things or events. Later, sometimes in a third stage, they may be viewed as dependent relationships between the people, things and events themselves. An example of the third stage is the previously described case of the boy who put out the light in order to extinguish the fire in his house. After so doing he could leave events to follow their magic course and go back to sleep (prelogical implications).

The superstitions and phobias belong to the first stage. The superstitious person who "knocks on wood" or performs other rituals knows that it is he who performs the act in order to ward off danger or evoke a happy event. The phobic patient knows he suffers from a morbid fear and relates it to himself. In neither is the contact with reality severed.

In sleep the ordinary dream corresponds to the second stage.

The nightmare is obviously related to the third stage.

[15] Except when the dreamer "dreams that he is dreaming."

Through such confusion, the law of magic participation becomes even more rigid; the bond between ideas and feelings on the one hand and the images on the other becomes even closer. I have called this *absolute participation*.

Indeed, the dreamer participates completely in the morbid images, even though he does not hold himself responsible for their existence or consequences. His increasing anxiety is sufficient proof of this.

A recent danger or unpleasant event may have the power to awaken and activate every link in a series of past painful memories down to the very earliest and traumatic ones. One condition is necessary for this "avalanche phenomenon" to occur: an associative relationship with the ever-present feeling of insecurity related to the feeling of powerlessness always present in these cases. I call this series of associations the descending chain of insecurity and powerlessness.

From the depths of sleep the earliest anxiety recurs to which all the secondary and ulterior anxieties in life have been added. So prepared, the nightmare is unavoidable.

The dreamer can resort to all possible defense mechanisms, logical and prelogical; he can call upon his instinct for self-preservation and his desire to live; but all these desperate efforts are in vain. His fate is settled; his death warrant has been signed as if by judicial process.

Stemming from the far past, primary anxiety drags with it all the most sinister contemporary images which resemble those that overwhelmed the child and early burdened him with phobias. Under the pressure of these representations, malevolent magic thinking is brought into action with the goal of producing a malevolent death. At times the dreamer is lured into believing that he is only a witness and not the culprit in the act, for example, that he is to attend a pleasant party only to receive the final blow at the last moment.

The nightmare reproduces the special characteristics of the first injuries from reality as they were experienced in the child's mind. These characteristics are betrayal, brutality, and the will to destroy.

As a more general principle we can say that the fearful child tends to fix his anxiety upon the most dangerous and offensive malevolent agents, the ones which most precisely annihilate his security. To my mind, this is the best psychogenic explanation of the strange phenomenon of primary masochism.

Salvation from malevolent death in the nightmare can be obtained by opposing the destructive power with a similar power working in the opposite direction. Such a power is positive magic thinking. However, a dynamic law prevents its use: the necessity of discharging a certain amount of anxiety. If positive magic thinking intervened, this carthartic function would be defeated and there would be no nightmare.

The nightmare is by nature "demoniac." Patients often call the perpetrators of their dream crimes their "devils." They may be things or humans—there is a relationship between the choice of symbol and the given mental structure. In any one patient, either cosmic images or human images predominate in the unconscious.[16] The reasons for this are historical and can be discovered by identifying the initial "devil," its nature and mode of intervention (violence, frequency of occurrences, etc.). In identifying this image, the child's situation in the family as well as his psychic and physical status must be evaluated.[17]

[16] The same predominance is found in myths and legends, as well as in children's stories—which so many adults like.

[17] Among the most traumatic diseases of childhood are asthma and whooping cough. Their paroxysms literally "descend upon" the child and are extremely painful. I have been able to relate certain nightmares of asphyxia to such memories.

Whooping cough is too lightly considered a "banal" disease of childhood. Its greatest trauma is due to two factors: (1) The paroxysm itself produces an

The first traumatic blows may have come either from things, animals, unhappy events or from people, especially parents and educators—and above all, from that omnipotent divinity called Mother. Although in general benevolent, the mother can at times play an evil role, for instance, when she, more or less voluntarily, helps weaken the feeling of security in her baby through impatience, scoldings, painful medical treatments, absences, or ignoring the child's needs during her own disturbed periods.

In the first case (things, animals or events), the plots of our patient's nightmares usually contain cosmic images. These may be terrestrial cataclysms, abysses, unbridled elements, fire, floods, sinister images of "dark, deep, engulfing waters," tempests, hurricanes, earthquakes, etc. There are the celestial cataclysms: lightning and meteors. Modern images of flying machines, half animal and half airplane, and terrible bombings occur. All these apocalyptic visions have been imagined by anxiety-ridden patients long before Bikini; the atom bomb now gives them only an appearance of scientific and rational justification.

There is also the theme of "the monsters": marine, terrestrial, celestial, or legendary monsters. They may be considered as animals. Others are the animals well known for their aggressiveness and cruelty (bears, lions, snakes, etc.). Such a monster often symbolizes cancer (see page 109).

The variety of malevolent objects is indefinite: trains, crashing autos, falling into abysses, sinking boats, etc.

In nightmares, fantasy freely elaborates on all themes. All the eschatological images have a common characteristic of horror and annihilation.

---

intense anxiety of a physiological origin. (2) The inevitable repetition of the paroxysms is a constant threat to the child and perpetuates in him the feeling of insecurity. Each attack makes him aware of his total powerlessness. Each new paroxysm recalls the preceding ones and increases the apprehension of subsequent ones. Here we again find the three Freudian elements of danger, powerlessness, and a memory. Parents should take special care of the psychic state of these little patients.

In the second case (people), we find survivals of certain "human images" in the nightmare. They are figures whose human nature is clear but whose identity remains indefinite. They can be classified into four categories according to their visual or moral character: (1) those of great size (see p. 110, the theme of gigantism); (2) those of brutal and sinister appearance: thieves, murderers, gangsters, Nazis, SS men, secret police, etc.; (3) those who show perfidy: the theme of the hidden creatures or the "invisible presence" which are thus all the more threatening— (somebody hidden under the bed, behind the curtain, the door, the window, in the next room or house; somebody roaming around; the door handle turning slowly; the appearance of a dagger or revolver held by an anonymous hand); (4) those that are supernatural: ghosts, spectres, spirits, the Devil, or demoniac spirits.

In common with the physical images, these magic incarnations have the characteristics of horror and annihilation. The nightmare contains a multitude of different images on the common background of terror, all being the various survivals of the same primary anxiety.

A Rule in Symptomatology

The choice of the dream image is not fortuitous or independent of the neurosis. The cosmic images with their physical manifestations characterize the neuroses where there is much survival of superstition and characterize the phobia. The survival of the human images with their psychic actions characterize the neurosis of abandonment.

Some Brief Examples

After his first attempts at sexual relations, a man related the following nightmare:

"I had a horrible nightmare. I am in bed; an indescribable

uproar breaks out—violent, cold drafts—the curtains swell out and float. Outside there is a cataclysm. The doors slam, the windows bang loudly. I awake screaming, 'Mother! Mother!' The scream awakened me. It took me a long time to get calmed down and I had to put on the light. It is incredible! I usually fear nothing!"

As a child, this patient had witnessed violent quarrels between his parents and shared their bedroom where for many years he witnessed their sexual intercourse. Since Freud, we have known that many children witnessing intercourse consider it an act of violence and aggression and attribute the sadistic role to the father. In his anxiety this patient had learned to hate and fear his father and, reacting to this, had identified with his mother. His own first unsuccessful sexual experience revived these early painful memories.

Nothing is more capable of suddenly throwing children into a state of mystery, worry, and insecurity than dissension between the parents, especially if the child believes himself to be the cause or the object of these quarrels. It is as if the child's naïve belief in an absolute love would be broken once and forever.

A woman, age thirty-five, relates a frequently recurring nightmare: "I am in a car with my husband. He is driving down a mountain road. The descent becomes steeper and steeper. Suddenly I know there is going to be an accident. It is certain. Instead of putting on the brakes, my husband steps on the accelerator. The car skids on the ice, turns over, and we plunge into the abyss."

Each time the dream is slightly different, but the theme remains the same. This is an example of the absoluteness of magic power. The belief that an accident will occur is immediately followed by its realization. The "coefficient of realization" is absolute.

The patient is a young girl. Her father, though a man of lofty principles, is brutal to her. She dreams, "I am on top of a tower of some sort of a castle. Far below there is a deep pond. I am not afraid because I am holding onto a solid battlement." ("Solid" or rational mechanism of defense.) "But—things change. I begin to think of getting dizzy. What if I should let go and fall?" (Malevolent magic thinking occurs. Rational measures are to no avail.) "At this very moment, a threatening man appears out of a trap door and pushes me off into empty space."

Here again, the dreamer dies at the time when she thinks of her death. The possible catastrophe becomes a certain one; the forseen fall occurs immediately. The simple effect of a subjective fear, the representation of danger, becomes the cause of the catastrophe. Exteriorized thought materializes. This is the same process as in the phobias. The superstitious person, even though he is fully awake, is prey to a similar illusion.

This patient lived in fear of her husband's infidelity. Eventually the fear increased into an obsessive dread that he would abandon her.

Resistances Coming from Things and People

The frustrations of life irritate "nervous" people more than others. Certain patients will develop anxiety when their desires and ambitions are thwarted by strong or obstinate resistance. These patients will tend to see an enemy in every object or person opposing them. They even go further, making a malevolent object of them. Does this occur in children?

A young man suffers from a chronic neurological disorder which keeps him in a state of great insecurity.[18] One day during winter, he started to light a fire in his fireplace. With his pathological clumsiness, he was incapable of managing the coal bucket. He finally gave up the battle with this refractory object

[18] Brain diseases are particularly apt to reduce security.

and, cold and exhausted, went to bed. He had the following nightmare: "I dreamed about a huge black bucket which looked at me with two big, black eyes. Its looks became more and more threatening as it rotated on its base, always staring at me and pursuing me wherever I went. I was very afraid and awoke in a panic!"

21. Nightmares and the Neurosis of Abandonment

To make the initial points clearer, we will begin with two dreams of a woman with a typical neurosis of abandonment. We will call her Ariane.

Adhering to the chronological order of her narration, we start with the first dream in which a benevolent person appears, and then go on to the second dream in which a terrifying, malevolent person appears. The second dream occurred shortly after the first.

"I am alone in a strange land. Before me a dark expanse of water spreads out endlessly. I feel afraid—a nothingness—before such immensity. But a god appears—a huge giant, half nude. I try to follow him, to attract his attention so that I can be under his protection. Then, showing me my family in deep mourning, he tells me: 'Stay with them, they also have nobody.' I awoke with a feeling of having a great mission to accomplish."

The family in mourning is her own, of course, and they are mourning over her death. In this dream, two opposing ideas, or better, feelings are expressed: the fear of death and the desire to live made all the stronger.

Death is the expanse of dark water, the immensity that attracts and engulfs the abandoned—the symbol of powerlessness and annihilation.

The deep and threatening waters represent the disappearance and destruction of the self. In the dream, the waters ended at the horizon where they touch the sky and are blended with it.

Beyond the dark waters is the pure light. The sky is the primitive symbol of eternal life and complete happiness, and of total security, too, because there death does not exist. Furthermore no one can chase you out of heaven once you are there—abandonment is impossible. The dark waters are transformed into light. And, of course, that such can occur is what we repeatedly tell our children.

That is why the dream ends with the situation so impressively reversed. The miracle is the work of the giant god, the great protector, who says, "No, you are not dead; go and comfort your family." It is the theme of resurrection. Risen from the dead, the dreamer is freed of her death anxiety and can now sleep peacefully without a nightmare. Her mission to comfort her family and perhaps protect them gives a new sense and value to her life. Having been excluded from her family circle (we will soon see how she got that idea), she now comes back into it as a benevolent person, not as an intruder. Her dream could not have offered a better solution to her fear of exclusion. The happy ending is simply the reversal of roles.

This brief interpretation is sufficient to emphasize the main idea of the dream: death and being condemned to die.

A few days later the patient had a horrible nightmare. The analysis of it brought her considerable relief. In this dream, through prelogical implication, her father is represented as a frog.

"I am on the terrace of our house lying on a sort of couch in a magnificent moonlight. Behind my head is a dark corridor instead of the living-room door. At the entrance of the corridor is a black frog, monstrous and horrible. I am seized with an inexpressible terror. Suddenly things change. Not the horrible frog, but my father emerges from the shadows of the corridor with a gun in his hand—like a common murderer. I feel paralyzed with fear! Awakening, I remained in the unpleasant atmosphere of my childhood and it was a long time before I could get out of it."

Some of the patient's associations to the nightmare were: "To me moonlight is both dark and full of light, made of both soft colors and threats, both appeasing and alarming. In my childhood, dark corridors terrified me."

Her father was an embittered, irascible and pessimistic widower. He saw threats, dangers, and possible accidents everywhere. He criticized and was given to anger and violence. Nothing—not even his frightened child—found grace in his eyes. Negative in everything, he typified a malevolent object for his daughter—the destroyer of affective values and, hence, of life itself.

For an unknown reason, he loved frogs and toads. Ariane found an excellent way of overcoming both her instinctive terror of these animals and her fear of her father: she identified herself with them. At least on the level of zoology some contact and understanding would be possible. She began to like frogs and toads. To tame them she would feed them worms which they took from her hand. In their garden they grew and multiplied. In the evenings she would play the flute to them. She thinks that she remembers that in the moonlight their croaking was louder, longer-lasting, shrill and soft at the same time. Her attempt to tame them is a good example of magic propitiation. Thus she would make friends and protegés of these strange and disgusting animals, and turn the malevolent beings into benevolent ones. Did she not emulate the snake charmers? Unfortunately she was much less successful with her terrible father and was never able to tame him. Whenever she tried to help him, to bring him his tea, he would rebuke, scold, and send her away. It is obvious why the frog and father are one in the nightmare.

The Theme of Exclusion and Intrusion

This theme consists of two opposing but related concepts.

1. On the terrace: Ariane is excluded from her father's house but remains in front of the door, strangely tied to the door by her head (by her mind, by her memories, and by her fears). The father-frog is close-by, ready to emerge from the shadows. This scene shows well the character of primary masochism in the childhood relationship of Ariane to her father.

Dark corridors had also been a phobogenic object for her.

2. The father armed with a gun: The terrace looked onto the garden; such an image would recall vivid anxiety-producing memories. She recalls how her father would frequently think he heard footsteps in the garden and would rush out to inspect. He had an exaggerated fear of thieves, quite in line with his whole personality.

Clearly in the nightmare Ariane identifies with the thieves, the intruders who forever seek to penetrate forbidden places.

Such ideas of exclusion and intrusion are two typical aspects of the complex of abandonment.

As time passed, the child lost all confidence in her father and, with that, lost all confidence in herself. The effect was catastrophic. Only her father had the power through his reassurance to give her assurance; but instead of giving it, he paralyzed her by overwhelming her with fears. Fear was always and everywhere. An alarming and dangerous mystery floated around the house—the mystery of life and death—of "to be or not to be." The discovery of the wickedness of her childhood gods was a trauma to the patient from which she never recovered. Security and protection from her family vanished. Faced with this impenetrable mystery, doubts, fears, and guilt feelings appeared. Depression and the desire to die were inevitable.

"And when I am dead, they will be very sorry, will regret their meanness toward me. Nobody will be able to comfort them. Only I could do that but I will be dead and gone. Yet I would so much want to see how my death affects them, to know how sorry they feel!"

The first dream is a second edition of this mournful infantile fantasy. The intervention of the benevolent deity allowed Ariane to satisfy her "need for verification." Can not death give love when life has withheld it?[19]

Ariane is not free to be herself, to give way to her needs and natural desires. Spontaneity, enthusiasm, tenderness—all these reactions are forbidden. She cannot yield to them and satisfy them, nor can she experience them consciously. Her tragic dilemma is that she either gives expression to these essential affective needs and is scolded, despised and rejected, suffering desperately, or she represses them and suffers from powerlessness and anxiety, and wishes to die. She is tempted to rid her father of her presence and to disappear forever.

"Father will throw me out and kill me!" These are the evil intentions she attributes to him. Often enough he has made her feel useless, superfluous, a nonentity. The one thing she could not understand was that, in his own way, he was suffering as much, if not more, than she. But to the child, adults do not suffer. They are all-powerful; only children suffer.

Ariane could not attribute any value to her own feelings, however intense and spontaneous, so long as her father denied them value. This was impossible because due to his realism the child is incapable of placing any value upon himself.

Parents should know of this difficulty with all its implications and dangers. Our patient, now an adult, has not acquired the right to experience her own feelings and consider them legiti-

---

[19] This is the theme of "verification of love through death." It will be studied further in the section on masochism in abandonment.

mate, valid, and healthy; and of course, she feels even less right
to express them.

It is easy to see that, for various reasons, anxiety was already
threatening when Ariane had the first dream. This dream had
the special purpose of preventing the development of anxiety
and of more nightmares. As we see, the mechanism did not work.

The two dreams together form an analytic whole which must
be reconstructed since the meaning of the beneficial dream illustrates the meaning of the nightmare.

In the good dream, she gives her father and whole family a
lesson. She opposes him with a more powerful and benevolent
being capable of annulling and making up for her sad childhood.
For the realization of such a wish, magic thinking is indispensable.

Thus Ariane imagined this omnipotent god, the master of sea,
heaven, space, time, and the life and death of unhappy children. Unhappy children will invent many such fantasies when
beset by insecurity.

With this example, I have indicated the deep and intrinsic
relationship between such nightmares and the neurosis of abandonment, and will discuss it further in Chapter X.

Further Analysis

The patient, Ariane, had suffered from a cancer phobia for
the past several years. For various reasons, the phobia had increased at the time in her analysis when the nightmare of the
frog and the murderous father occurred.

Freud discovered that in dreams in general the symbol is over-
determined, that is, has several meanings all associatively related
to each other. The same is true of Ariane's black frog. Undoubt-
edly, this horrible animal also symbolized cancer of the womb.
The association between her fear of cancer and her father's
cruelty was later elaborated. Originally the father was the love

object; but he forbade feelings, and more specifically, forbade that she have any feelings for him. The destruction of the affective life dragged the sexual life with it. Killing love, the father also killed the instinct. His malevolent power was represented by a new weapon in the cancer, similar to the revolver in the dream. Both these symbols stand for a long past of suffering in this woman's life. In fact, all the patients with cancer phobia that I have seen have had painful and joyless childhoods.

Let us once again point out the utter powerlessness of the ego during a nightmare. The ego has no defense against the magic thinking which has planned its death and destruction. During the day, the patient can defend himself through reason, action, or "knocking on wood"; the agoraphobic can stay at home; and others, like Ariane, consult psychiatrists.

The Macroscopic Phenomenon and the Giant Theme

Here is a verbatim example of this type of dream: "My dream takes place in my parents' bedroom. Before me I see a thin and emaciated man. I don't know why, but I am furious at him and begin to abuse him. Suddenly he becomes bigger and bigger, taller and taller—enormous, gigantic—a giant. I begin to stutter; but the more I want to insult him, the more I stammer. Words stick in my throat. I awaken in a state of horrible anxiety, still wanting to insult him."

This phenomenon is frequent in the neurosis of abandonment and supplies strong evidence of the relationship between insecurity and feelings of powerlessness in primary anxiety. The colossal god in Ariane's dream likewise points to a functional interpretation of these macroscopic images. Their function is to translate subjective reactions, which can only be expressed in abstract terms, into sensorial language (the only language accessible in dreams) and concrete terms. Two mechanisms must be considered: the increase in size as well as the ultimate size.

1. The increase in the size of the malevolent object expresses the increase in the feelings of insecurity and helplessness of the subject.

2. An extreme immensity of the object expresses a total loss of security and power in the subject. It illustrates the absolute character of his state of *a*security and powerlessness. Immensity is a perfect visual expression of the idea of the absolute. If the patient attributes an infinite greatness to the subject in his dreams, he is making us understand that he also attributes absolute power to that object, just as children impute these qualities to objects and people, especially parents and educators.

In the above dream, the giant was a condensed image of the parents of the patient as he "saw" them during his childhood. His parents were extremely authoritarian and unmerciful. They turned him into a fearful child, and later, with the development of anxiety, into a neurotic one.

Wherever there is a giant, there is a dwarf. Before a giant, one feels very small and expects to be crushed; as one patient said, "like a flea in front of an elephant."

The giant is a striking dream symbol of the objectification of the complement. The "complementary attribute" is a huge, gigantic fear, the fear of physical destruction, of death. The all-powerful, threatening giant is a typical symbol of powerlessness and, hence, an outstanding malevolent symbol. Behind its immensity, the macroscopic image hides innumerable unpleasant memories and traumatic experiences which are at the basis of primary anxiety. From this viewpoint, the malevolent giant can be called an "absolute object," depending on the patient's concept of it.

This patient's dream is interesting from many angles. It expresses a complex psychological process through a rather simple physiological mechanism. More exactly, it expresses a psychic inhibition through an organic reflex inhibition. "The insulting words stuck in my throat instead of passing my lips." This is an adequate and ingenious symbolic mode of expression through which we understand the child's desperate efforts to "keep inside" his legitimate anger and eventually to repress all reactive aggression, be it ever so justified.

To the dreamer, his nightmare is an excruciatingly vivid, alive and actual experience. It is directly lived because in his sleep he ignores that it is actually being relived. Its burning reality cannot be denied by reducing it to an interplay of symbols. One cannot say to a patient, "Your nightmare (or phobia) is only the symbolic expression of infantile illusions." This would ignore the essential problem and only shock or annoy the patient. Interpretation of the symbolism of a dream is only half the work, and therefore might lead to therapeutic failure.

In phobias and nightmares, the attacks are not just a form of some outdated childish language; they are the actual expression of the patient's anxiety. However, this expression borrows its characteristics from the reawakened primary anxiety. Phobias and nightmares draw their real strength from the living, moving sources of the original fears of man—hence, their acute intensity; hence also their discrepancy with the measure of security which reason, science, and modern society are supposed to provide for the civilized individual.

This brief analysis of phobias and anxiety dreams permits two comments to be made. The first concerns the well-known phenomenon of "adherence." The relationship between the subject and phobogenic object, between the dreamer and the persecutor, consists of a double and simultaneous action of attraction and repulsion. Even while he flees from it, the subject clings to this object. One patient called this magic adherence "sticking." "I stick to the policemen who are searching for me." Or: "A huge bull comes toward me—I quickly scramble up a big, vertical wall

—as soon as I am on the top, there is the bull waiting for me—
and so on." Such neurotic adherence is a striking example of
negative affective participation. Provoked by fear and aggression,
it originates in primary masochism and actually defines it.

One last word on the interpretation of the processes of thought
and affectivity in dreams. In both ordinary dreams and nightmares, this kind of psychogenic interpretation must remain in
close contact with the "life of the ego." We try to come as close
as possible to the lived experience, systematically interpreting its
proper setting in the remote past. This experience consists of a
double current, the influence of reality on the subject and the
subject's reaction to reality. In childhood, these reactions do not
become conscious, as too many parents and educators still believe,
but are expressed through objectification. That objectification
and consciousness are mutually exclusive is an important part of
Piaget's teaching.

PART TWO

THE EGO AND PRELOGICAL REGRESSION IN NEUROSES

CHAPTER THREE

THE REALISM OF DREAMS

INTRODUCTION

In the preceding part, I have attempted to apply the data of genetic psychology to the analysis of certain neurotic symptoms. My goal was to emphasize the role of anxiety in producing regression to the prelogical stage of infantile thinking. In this part, I will attempt to apply the same data to the study of the more general phenomenon of the structure and psychological nature of neuroses.

Regression in neuroses is selective and circumscribed and can also be intermittent, manifesting itself in crises of variable lengths and frequencies. Being selective and partial, regression respects a part of the ego which then remains refractory to the neurotic process. In this refractory area, the principles of logical thinking and what can be called the rational principles of affectivity remain intact and are correctly applied.[1]

[1] The current idea of "reasonable" needs and emotions presupposes the intervention of intelligence and the influence of reason on the affective life. I cannot go into the problem but merely want to point to this principle which is emphasized by the genetic psychologists.

By nature, affective needs are pressing and often imperiously so. This is a striking feature of the neurosis of abandonment where the need for security demands immediate satisfaction and the need for love requires categorical reassurance. These demands impede reflection on and judgment of the future. In entering a love relationship, the subject hardly evaluates the remote consequences at all.

It is in the evaluation of the future that the rational functions of the ego must intervene. Their main role is a kind of anticipation of the consequences of a certain behavior. However, to be guided by rational principles means that one must be a relatively good master of one's affectivity. Such mastery requires a good coordination between the ego functions (as we defined them in the Introduction) and the intellectual and logical aptitudes.

117

In my interpretation of the ego structure, the ego is divided into two areas: one leads to normal, psychic activity and behavior patterns, the other is regressed and infantile. In the analysis of the behavior of phobic patients, I have called these zones sectors of the ego.

The idea of sectors is here defined by the *logical* or by the *prelogical* character of the psychic activity.[2] This implies that the ego has a structure; and indeed, one could not speak of regressed phenomena of thought if there did not exist a psychological structure necessarily inferior to the level of thought before the regression. Therefore it is important accurately to define this concept of structural regression in the totality of the facts and processes which make up the "life of the ego."

Regression cannot be total, otherwise disorganization would occur, not neurosis. Neurotic regression is always partial, affecting only a circumscribed part of psychic activity and thus damaging only one special relationship between the subject and reality. In other words, the subject behaves in a regressed and infantile way only in relation to a certain element in the external world or social environment.

Can we attribute to the phenomenon of prelogical, or paralogical, regression a general value in psychopathology? The purpose of this section is to give a more precise definition of its functional role.

Our thesis is that the ego is dissociated in the neuroses. This affirmation raises several questions: Why this dissociation? What is its origin? Is there a necessary relationship between the evolution and appearance of the neurosis and the production of this structural dissociation in the ego? And a final question must be

[2] The term "paralogical" might be suggested for the regression of the neurotic adult. This would emphasize the differences between the prelogic of the child and adult neurotic "paralogic." These differences are due to the general development of the personality; for instance, the neurotic adult never completely lacks "social feelings" (solidarity, cooperation, reciprocity, etc.).

raised. Most neuroses arise from repressions occurring during childhood. The etiological importance of this process cannot be denied. Does this have any relationship to the processes of ego dissociation and is this relationship of a genetic nature? These are the problems to be defined and answered.

A priori, it seemed to me important to consider not only the general phenomenon of neuroses but also the particular phenomenon of dreams. Since Freud, we have known of the functional and dynamic relations that exist between the two. Applying the study of dreams to the data of genetic psychology will bridge a gap in psychoanalytic theory.

This consideration brings up further questions. Is there a real relationship between the dream mechanisms of the neurotic adult and the mechanisms of infantile prelogic? If so, to what does this relationship owe its existence and what are its characteristics?

All these questions center around primary realism. A neurosis is the whole of disorders affecting thought, emotions, and behavior. All these neurotic phenomena are due to regressed activity of the ego during the waking state. A dream is the best example of regressed activity of the ego, at least of that part of the ego which does not sleep but dreams.

These two orders of phenomena, neuroses and dreams, have one common feature of obvious interest, and their combined study provides a better understanding of their psychogenetic aspects. Let us begin with the clearer and less doubtful data given by the analysis of dreams which will complete the previous analysis of nightmares.

NOTE ON REGRESSION AND FIXATION

As will be elaborated later, the concept of regression has two different meanings:

1. It defines a relation between two given structures. One

structure is said to be regressed in comparison with another structure considered to be normal or progressive. In certain areas and at certain times, the ego's activity shows characteristics that we call infantile. This diagnosis can be made because, in another area at another time, this activity is that of an adult. This concept of regression is founded on contrast. One area can be called regressed only in relation to another which is not.

2. In its second meaning, the regressed activity is considered in itself as being infantile, and we speak of a fixation, not a regression. Analysis of the patient shows that in everything concerning a certain sector of activity, he remains fixated at an infantile stage. On this point, his ego has not progressed. Since this area has not participated in the evolution of the healthy part of the ego, it cannot be said to have regressed. There is no regression but rather a nonevolution. Hence it would be more correct to speak of a nonevolved sector instead of a regressed one; however, the latter term is more practical and clearer in the study and description of the neuroses. In observing a neurotic patient, we are struck by the fundamental discord which exists between two simultaneous or alternating ways of thinking and behaving, one evolved, the other nonevolved.

22. The Two Aspects of Dreams

When we sleep we lose all sense of reality, which shades off and vanishes. Reality no longer exists except our subjective reality as contrasted to the objective reality which surrounds us in the waking state.

From the description of the above-mentioned dreams one fact is evident: they use an integral realism. Anxiety dreams and nightmares adequately demonstrate this. A black frog can only inspire such terror if it is truly believed to exist. I asked Ariane during a session: "Try to visualize the animal with all the characteristics of the dream. What do you feel?" She answered, "Oh, nothing, a slightly unpleasant, even a little amused feeling." The integral realism of the dreamer is due to ignorance. When we sleep we are perfectly unaware of the regressed nature of our thinking, and therefore of the absolute subjectivity of the wishes and fears which we experience in the dream. Without hesitation, we attribute these fears and feelings to the things and people moving, acting and living on the stage created by our dreams. Only when awake are we able to re-establish the correct causality of the dream phenomena and attempt its analysis, although not always, or at least not at once, correctly. We often need a certain time to awaken fully and to dispel the realistic illusions which sleep has imposed upon us. This time of recovery varies much with individuals and the types of dreams. It is longest after a nightmare where we have the greatest difficulty in getting back to reality despite the relief of awakening.

Up to now, psychiatrists have generally limited the study of dreams to Freudian interpretations. Such a study should be completed by probing into the genetic aspects of the dream phenomenon. To be complete, both aspects must be combined.

Two kinds of elements must be considered: on the one hand, the energies (drives or instincts) and the affects which they determine; on the other hand, the psychic mechanisms used by and specific to dream thinking.

Freud has emphasized the former. His theory is well known: the dream is the symbolic or disguised realization of a repressed wish, or, in a second category of dreams, an attempt to annul a fear and its consequences. This theory is verified every day in psychotherapy. However, how can a wish be expressed and then realized during sleep when nothing is real any more?

Wish fulfillment in dreams occurs through a number of mechanisms described by Freud, such as symbolism, displacement, condensation, etc.[3] These desires first intrude upon the ego in a rather incoherent and dissociated form. The ego's task then is to transform the raw material it has at its disposal into a coherent and comprehensible whole: to create a "plausible" story which can be told. This effort toward synthesis and logic has been called by Freud "secondary elaboration of dreams." It could also be called the contribution of the ego to the formation of dreams. In this second form, the dream finally penetrates consciousness.

However, it was Piaget who pointed out the very realistic (in the genetic sense of the term[4]) character of the ego process in the dream. Every dream can be interpreted according to Freud or to Piaget.

For example, a typical dream: "I am in a dark hall, probably a movie theater, and watch a movie showing aviation scenes. Then, it is as if the movie were my dream or my dream continued in the movie. I find myself in an airplane which I try to steer. I am very afraid when I see enemy planes come nearer and open fire. . . ."

Here is a brief formulation of realism in this dream: we believe while dreaming that things actually happen as they happen in the dream. The dream of the movie which then becomes the dream itself is a good demonstration of this.

When dreaming we do not locate themes and images in our mind or head. The dream unfolds itself in the very places evoked by these images, in the very scenery which we imagine. We make a threefold confusion which we can dispel only after awakening: confusion between internal and external; between sign and the thing signified (dream symbolism); and between thought and matter, or the representation and its object. Moreover, psychic motivation (the wish to fly) and the physical realization (flying

[3] See Freud's *Interpretation of Dreams,* 1900.
[4] See the author's discussion of the use of the word "realism" and of Piaget's concept of "realism" on page 11 to 14.

an airplane during an air fight) are totally undifferentiated. The ego, projecting itself into the universe and localizing in external reality the elements it has elaborated, confuses itself with this reality. The ego is led to this illusion through magic thinking. In order to govern the world and people, the dreamer changes them and makes them act according to his needs, wishes and fears. Scenery and actors are pure elements of the unconscious, manipulated by the ego and visualized in an illusory space. Wish and truth are one, appearance and being are confounded. There is no dualism.

Infantile realism is thus fully activated and integrated by the dream. Without this realism, the secondary elaboration would be impossible and inconceivable.

23. Realism and Freud's Theory

One question can be raised when considering Freud's theories on dreams. Even though asleep, the mind can experience full satisfaction of desires which are repressed or suppressed when awake. Evidently such satisfaction can only be purely hallucinatory. But in our dreams we have real feelings and even the absolute certainty of a real satisfaction. How can we confuse in such a way a pure hallucination with an absolute certainty? How can we mistake the objects of our hallucinatory perceptions for completely real phenomena?

The answer seems simple. The confusion is due to primary realism, to the lack of dualism (in the Baldwinian sense). The dream of the adult can be defined by this integral or complete realism. Without integral realism there can be no dream; except in dreams, there is no integral realism. From this it is only a short step to affirm that the condition of the dream process is a regression to the infantile level of thought. This regression is determined by sleep. However, it is known that such a regression can also occur during the waking state, although never so completely. Neurotic symptoms which do not show some primary realism are very infrequent, if they occur at all.

In neuroses such a regression is an anomaly; during sleep it is a normal phenomenon. When asleep, we do not suspect how far back into childhood our thinking has gone. Does this mean that we really yearn for this childhood with all its naïve and convenient realism? Our dreams, so constant and universal, could lead us to believe so. However, such an explanation would be pseudo scientific and would bestow an affective finality on the activity of the unconscious. Instead of explaining it, a further indisputable fact must be considered.

In inhibiting our objective perception of things, sleep also inhibits the more evolved modes of thinking. It allows only a purely subjective perception of phenomena and so re-establishes primitive intellectual modes of thinking. These modes are always latent in us. If awakening banishes them, sleep awakens them. Infantilism potentially exists in every adult.

What has been said thus far seems clear but not complete. Since Freud and Piaget, the science of dreams has made incontestable progress, but many mysteries remain unexplained. This young science is at the border of biology, physiology and psychology. The psychologists have now made their contributions and are waiting for further help from biologists and physiologists. This is why, with our present-day knowledge, all theories about dreams can only be partial, depending on the viewpoint from which the phenomenon is considered: in its relation to affective life with its conflicts and repressions; or as part of the physiological and biological phenomenon of sleep. In our ignorance no complete theory is yet possible.

My contribution emphasizes that, on the psychological level, *dream realism* is an essential fact; it completes the affective dynamisms of the dream as described by Freud. Without realistic thought coupled with magic thinking, there can be no dreams, phobias or superstitions. On the other hand, there is no dream thinking without its affective dynamisms. Affect is the power, thought the instrument of dreams.

Prelogical regression is characteristic of the dreams of the most socialized and civilized individual. Whether an individual is intelligent and educated or not, his dreams will always be a monument to illogical thinking and infantilism.

24. On Piaget's Study of Dreams

In his fundamental work on infantile realism, Piaget devoted one chapter to dreams.[5] He distinguished three stages of dream development: (1) From five to eight years: "The dream comes from the exterior and remains exterior to the mind." The dream emanates from things or people, in other words, from the images which come to the child's mind while dreaming. (2) From eight to twelve years: "The dream originates from us but is exterior to us . . . The image of a person remains related to this person through participation so long as this person is not a subjective representation of the sleeper." (3) The dream is interior and of internal origin.[6]

Thus it appears that in the child younger than ten to twelve years "the dream is localized on the spot where it carries us. If one dreams about a man who is in the street, the dream is in the street." It takes place "under my window." This is primary realism, confusion between being and appearance: the dream seems to be in the street, therefore it is in the street.[7]

In other words, if in dreams the imagination invents place, moment, scenery and actors, the young child still believes on

[5] *La représentation du monde chez l'enfant.* Chapter III, pp. 69 ff.
[6] *Ibid.*, p. 100.
[7] *Ibid.*, p. 78.

awakening that his dream has really happened in this place, at this moment, that the actors have really existed and played their roles. While he tells us his dreams, the child does not correct this realistic or externalistic illusion. "This belief in the exterioralization of the images of dreams is very resistant."[8] Indeed this belief is much more resistant than most child psychologists would have believed.

Psychoanalysts working with adults are very often struck by the resistance of realism in all its forms, especially in its moral form (i.e., the infantile superego), and its constant reappearance often creates serious difficulties in therapy. In our patients, the constant tendency to fall back on the realistic conception of dreams, even when awake, is but one aspect, and one of the most interesting, of the neurotic externalism characteristic of their nonevolved thinking. Of course, when awake they do not fall back to the first stage described by Piaget but usually regress to the second stage, except in certain particular circumstances, for instance, when the mind is still confused after awakening from a nightmare. When they recall their dreams and nightmares for us, or better, relive them, many patients, like children eight to ten years of age, relapse into the realistic illusion in which they were during sleep. At times, it looks as if they were still asleep. A few examples of such relapses follow:

1. Before telling the dream of this thirty-five-year-old patient, I wish to call attention to his spontaneous remark at the end of his story. He is a highly intelligent man with a neurosis characterized by heteronomy and a father complex. The dream was one of emancipation. The patient's remark (italicized) was not part of the dream text but was later added by him.

"I am with my girl friend. My father who is in the house suddenly comes in and preaches morals to me . . . *speaks about*

8 *Ibid.*, p. 78.

certain principles . . . but I pretend I am right—*How can anyone have such ideas!"*

Actually no such conversation on morals ever took place between this father and his son.

2. "My dream takes place in the country in a very pleasant place. I admire the green hills; there are some flowers in the valley where I am. In the neighborhood there is a farm with its barns. The farmers come and go; laborers work. It is a peaceful, pastoral atmosphere. Suddenly everything changes. The rumor spreads that a wild bull is loose in the country. Panicky, I run away and take refuge in a church . . . I close the door quickly behind me."

I said to the patient, "Here again is your old fear of malevolent beings . . ."

"But, doctor, . . . I was not the only one who was afraid and fled. All the farmers were afraid too, as much as I was, even though they were farmers used to these animals and for whom a bull would not be malevolent."

And he goes on insisting on the collective character of the panic!

The bull symbolizes his sexual drives and new desires for adventure. These desires fill him with anxiety. Unable to fight them, he is afraid that their satisfaction will ruin his health. Besides this, he is plagued with doubts and insecurity. "I don't know where they [his wishes] are going to lead me," he often repeats, "but they will certainly land me in some trouble . . ."

In this dream, the patient is saying that all men are made anxious by their sexual wishes and that they are a deadly force for everybody. As the genetic psychologists well know, the child never doubts that others feel exactly as he does.

3. A married woman, unhappy because of her husband's lack of attention and affection, dreams: "I am desperately clinging to a rock during a difficult and dangerous bit of mountain climbing.

My husband is ahead of me . . . but he goes on climbing without paying any attention to me in spite of my calls [abandonment]. I can neither climb nor descend. Suspended over the abyss, terrified, I cry, 'Julius, Julius!' but he does not answer . . ." And she adds in a furious tone of voice: "It was awful . . . You see how this husband of mine is. He is simply criminal. His only desire is to see me dead . . ."

I could only comment, "You seem to forget that it is not your husband who had the dream."

4. A young girl relates the following dream with increasing bitterness and violence.

"In my dream, I am in a little rowboat surrounded by rocks. I am afraid. My mother appears on the shore. *She* has a mean look, starts to yell at me, shakes her fist and makes horrible faces. *She* abuses me. Then *she* throws a big thing into the water that raises a huge wave. *She* directs this wave toward me with well-calculated, slow gestures. I see the mass of water hurl over me and drown me. I shout to the witch: Stop, stop! But deaf to my pleas, *she* does not listen. On the contrary, with a mocking smile, *she* makes me understand that *she* has decided on my death." And the patient added, "In reality, I have suspected for a long time that she's wanted me dead. . . Isn't it terrible for a mother to wish for her daughter's death?"

I said, "But note that you, and not your mother, created this dream and imagined your magic murder."

5. A young man, age twenty-eight, with repressed sexual drives, dreams:

"I am taking a walk with Marianne at night in the woods. I want to go home quickly because I am afraid that my mother is going to ask for explanations. But Marianne takes one of my hands and puts it around her waist, then takes the other and puts it around her neck. There we are, tenderly embraced." Then he adds, "Isn't that just like these modern young girls!"

The telling of these dreams is often accompanied by violent affects, experienced with all their power, the very power which forced the patients to repress them. The upsurge of these affects into consciousness thus reactivates the realistic processes of thought in the telling of the dream as well as in the dream itself. Telling the dream revives the dream and the dream revives the affect. This is the interesting fact.

In passing, let us point out another fact. Certain individuals attempt spontaneously to correct these realistic illusions while still dreaming. Instead of just dreaming, they "dream that they dream." "In my dream I tell myself that I am only dreaming." "I dream that I am acting, but at the same time, I witness the scene as a spectator, somewhat like in a movie." "You are telling me a story and at the same time I see what you are describing."

"I dream that I dream" means precisely that it is imaginary, untrue. I will come back to this phenomenon later in a note concerning the "corrected dreams" (p. 210).

Summary. In remembering their dreams, patients can make them seem alive, give them full reality. The imagined people are animate; their intentions become real, emanating from them, not from the dreamer. This is magical participation. While recalling a dream, the memory and reliving of the dream emotions cause a sudden and short-lived relapse into realism. In adults, these relapses correspond to attacks of externalism, related to the dream and connected with affects, usually negative affects. This is especially true of nightmares. It is the affect which determines the brief disorder of thought on awakening, not the reverse.

When a child explains his dream still using his prelogical thinking, the child is logical with himself. But it is abnormal for an adult to return to realistic illusions when he tells his dreams. The term of externalism seeks to define this anomaly; or in a less

abridged way, it may be defined as the regressive mode of ex-
teriorizing thoughts and affects.

25. THE PSYCHOTHERAPEUTIC EFFECT OF A LECTURE ON THE REALISM OF DREAMS

In his chapter on the dreams of children, Piaget mentioned an
interesting incident that happened to one of his students. "This
student believed throughout part of her childhood that her parents had attempted to drown her in the sea."[9] When I later met
this person, I asked her for more details of her realistic adventure.
Here is a summary of her answer: "As a child I always believed
that I was worth nothing in the eyes of my parents. About the
age of four or five years, I had the following dream: 'I fall into
the sea and I am drowning, falling deep down into the black
water. It is night. Above me a few yards on the wharf, I see the
silhouette of my parents tenderly embracing each other. They
know that I am drowning . . . but do nothing to save me . . .'
"For a long time I really believed that this had happened; that
I really was about to drown under their eyes and that they had
not come to help me. I would think about this once in a while;
for instance when my father was nice, I asked myself: 'How
could he do such a thing?' I thought that there was a contradiction between his show of affection and his desire to see me die by
drowning. Then later, I forgot about it. However, although I
forgot this painful memory, the thing stuck somewhere in my
mind.

"Much later, I listened to a fascinating lecture by Professor
Piaget on the realism of dreams. During a walk after the lecture,
while thinking about the amazing problems brought out by Professor Piaget, I suddenly became conscious of and remembered
the dream of drowning and the stupendous indifference of my

[9] *Ibid.*, p. 73.

parents. 'How silly I am,' I said to myself, 'It was only a dream!' It took me quite a while to admit it completely, so vivid and clear in my memory was the silhouette of my parents. I still can see them while thinking about it today. This sudden realization provoked an emotional shock of stupefaction and relief at the same time: stupefaction for having so long held such a monstrous thing as real; relief because I now know that my parents were incapable of such a deed and that they loved me more than I had thought. . ."

As we see, this is a typical example of a dream of abandonment. It is characteristic of such childhood nightmares to leave deep and ineffaceable impressions. Forgetting cannot cancel them. The realistic illusions they generate are so strong that in this instance, a psychology student was able to maintain them intact until she learned about the existence of the realism of dreams.

From the viewpoint of psychology, or considered in its relation to ego psychology, a dream consists in an attack of regression of thought during sleep. All the modes and characteristics of prelogical thought as well as of the affects related to and animating this thought are represented in a dream. They are manifested in a "pure state," infinitely combined. They owe this unconditional freedom to the fact that sleep, on the one hand, produces a total break between mind and reality, consciousness and the world of objects, and on the other hand, gives the unconscious access to the ego.

Basically, a dream recognizes only one law which guarantees its existence and the realization of its goals. This is the law of infantile realism. In this respect, a dream is the only phenomenon capable of realizing complete accord between adult consciousness and prelogical thought. This accord means that the ego and the unconscious thoughts join again on this prelogical level. There is "homonomy" because logical thought is inhibited. This homonomy seems to give the best explanation for the global character of regression in dreams.

Is the same true for neuroses, or better, for the ego of neurotic adults and their ego activities during the waking state?

Freud discovered the close relationship between neurosis and dreams. The neurotic symptom and the dream are two related phenomena and this relationship is of a functional order. Both are a kind of search for compromise. The symptom is a compromise between the repressed and the superego; the dream, between repressed, superego and ego. In this compromise, desire, fear, drives, and demands are expressed. This is the dynamic aspect, instinctive and affective, of the relation between the two phenomena. Beyond this, they have in common their structure and the regression to a realistic level. The regression is total in dreams, partial in neuroses. The similarity between their structures is one more argument in favor of Freud's theory.

Note. It would seem logical to have these considerations followed by a paragraph on a particular form of realism of which I have already spoken: *affective realism.*

It is part of the general symptomatology of neuroses, but its role is most important in the neurosis of abandonment. The reasonings and strange behavior of these patients provide us with the best examples of affective realism. They are indispensable documents for the understanding of the realistic modes of affectivity in adults. For their description, see Chapter VIII.

CHAPTER FOUR

THE STRUCTURAL DUALISM OF THE EGO

Introduction

Following the discussion of dreams, we can now turn to the principle of partial and selective regression and its consequences, mentioned in the Introduction to Part II. Such regression results in the division of the ego into two parallel but discordant functional systems. These systems are regulated by contradictory laws which necessarily lead to a clear-cut state of dissociation.

It is precisely this phenomenon of dissociation in neuroses that I define as the structural dualism of the ego.

As I have tried to show, in dreams the thought process is regulated solely by realistic principles. Its only law is infantile prelogic. This is *homonomy*. The same cannot exist in neuroses. As soon as the individual awakens, there is *antinomy*. Antinomy defines the phenomenon of structural dualism of the ego when, in the waking state, there is opposition between the logical and paralogical principles used alternately by the subject to cope with reality.

To highlight these concepts I will later present a number of characteristic cases. First, however, it is necessary to discuss the two most clear-cut examples of functional dissociation found in psychopathology.

26. The Prelogic Sector and Phobia

No phenomenon illustrates the dualism of the ego better than do the phobias. In the phobic patient we easily recognize the double action of a regressed sector alternating with a normal and well-adjusted sector which can be called the *progressive* sector. The dissociation is evident.

The activity of the progressive sector aims at adjustment to reality. Its principle is the integration of the data of reality or, as Piaget says, its assimilation. Assimilating the data of reality and adjusting to reality are the two essential and correlated tasks of every individual who wishes to be well adapted to his environment. In neuroses the presence of antinomy renders a complete and lasting adaptation impossible. Adjustment can only be partial or intermittent, depending on whether the patient is progressing or regressing. In the regressed sector, the normal interplay of ego functions is severely disturbed if not completely blocked.

Where the phobia is active, the lack of adjustment to reality is complete. Instead of adjusting himself to reality, the subject integrates reality into his affective scheme. To be more exact, once infantile affectivity is reanimated, it incites the subject to invest certain elements of the external world with paralogical attributes. These elements are the phobogenic objects, and the phobic illness results from the unconquerable fear inspired by these malevolent objects.

Free and calm reflection must govern mature action. The phobic patient is incapable of two indispensable operations: the rational search for the objective causes of real phenomena, and the search for the subjective causes of psychic phenomena. All neurotic patients suffer from a lack of these two aptitudes whenever a regressed sector is operating.

Thus, in neurosis, infantile affectivity inhibits rational operations. This inhibition is characteristic of every neurotic symptom; it particularly conditions and explains the "affective participation" between subject and phobogenic object. Every affective participation presupposes adualism and thus undermines the foundations of logic.

In the regressed areas, the subject interprets reality according to the emotions he experiences. Objective judgments are inaccessible to him. In the progressive sector, on the contrary, he adapts his emotions to reality and submits them to the norms of objectivity and logic. Action guided by reflection and logic is adjusted and efficient. Only such an action can break through the realistic or paralogical affective structure which exists in pure phobias.

In the phobic patient, thinking is overwhelmed by emotions and governed by affects. This is why logical analysis is impossible. Instead of objectifying reality, the patient does the contrary; he objectifies his fear of reality by projecting into reality the aggression which is the positive completive attribute of his negative affect, i.e., his fear of aggression. In phobias, this mechanism is essential. It summarizes almost completely the ideo-affective activity of the patient when he experiences the malevolent and paralogical atmosphere which surrounds the phobogenic object, be it a pencil, a blackened bit of paper, cars or mice. This paralogical attitude closely resembles the prelogical attitude of the child, with the difference, however, that in the adult this attitude is only manifested in the sector surrounding the phobogenic object and its magical force.

The phobic patient appears as a kind of anxious god who constructs a malevolent reality to which he then adjusts himself as well as possible. The patients with obsessions or superstitions proceed inversely in that they construct their magical actions and thinking and later adjust the malevolent reality to them. They rule the cosmos through the omnipotence which they attribute to their propitiatory formulas and their rituals; they become overly individualistic. However, in the face of their anxiety-producing object, the phobic patients lose control of their minds, of their autonomy.[1] Before this mortal danger, all introspection becomes impossible because the causes of anxiety are unconscious. These causes can only be sought for by the phobic patient outside himself and his consciousness. He believes that he can find them in an external element which he then turns into a symbol; later he confuses symbol and element, attributing to the latter the magical force and power of the former. Symbolic thought replaces rational thinking. These psychic processes have all the qualities of infantile and primitive mentality.

For example, a woman is overtaken by panic in a restaurant. The sudden anxiety forces her to flee. From then on, this restaurant and later all restaurants are considered to be sources of danger and misfortune. She is absolutely forbidden to enter any of them. They are no longer pleasant and hospitable places for dining; they have lost their logical value.

Summary. A regressed sector simply means that a certain part of the ego has fallen back to a more primitive level than the one it had reached before the outbreak of anxiety. In the above example, we may speak of a restaurant sector; with Lucy, of a car sector. In both cases, a more primitive level means the magic symbolic stage of projection of the completive attribute.

Restaurants and streets are spatial notions. In other cases, as we will see, time notions may also be involved in the regressed sector.

SECTORS AND NEUROTIC MOMENTS

To speak of a sector is to use a simple image with a spatial characteristic. In reality the idea of sector also covers the temporal idea of "time" and practically is confused with it, as I have indicated previously when speaking of the intermittency of regres-

---

[1] This remarkable contrast is due to the fact that in phobias regression is deeper and more total. In the obsessional neurosis, the subject is not led through regression to the level of primary anxiety (see later).

sion. At a certain moment, the subject shows social logic; at another moment, social prelogic. At times he sticks to the first system, at times to the second, passing easily from one to the other. These changes depend on external and internal factors, on people with whom the subject meets and relates, or more often, with whom he cannot relate. Most often these factors are affective relationships with their difficulties.

FANTASIES AND THE REGRESSED SECTOR

Reactivation of prelogical thinking is closely related to disappointments and dissatisfaction. To compensate for the denial of their wishes, many patients drift into daydreams and fantasies. Fantasies owe their reparative function to magic thinking which can give them an almost total "coefficient of reality." Each fantasied idea is free to develop all its consequences, and the relief and joy of the daydreamer can turn into euphoria. Fiction seems real or really lived. This is why the habit of daydreaming becomes irresistible; the daydreamer gives in to it, just as a drug addict to his favorite drug.

The process underlying the fabrication of fantasies characterizes a special kind of regressed sector in which, as in dreams, realism reigns.

At times, an obsessional neurotic relapses into his obsessions without any valid external reason. Internal disturbances also determine symptoms and crises in certain patients. At any rate, the two concepts of sector and time cannot be dissociated. We can say that at a certain time a certain sector begins to function.

Projection renders the action on reality inefficient and the ego turns away from adjustment to reality. To project one's ego into reality is to give reality power over the ego. Patients with phobias prove this every day. As soon, however, as they stop projecting they again dominate reality.

Lucy used to repeat, "Where *I* am concerned [that is, my real, well-adjusted ego, my normal sector], I would fear nothing . . . if only there were no crushers everywhere . . ." She was able to prove this by her exploits in mountaineering.

In every regressed sector a certain psychic system is at work. This system is a functional whole. In adults the central source of regression or its *primum movens* is not this concept or that; it is an affect. The affect determines the use of prelogical concepts, not the reverse.

Freed of anxiety, the phobic patient is freed from his paralogic thinking. He recovers a normal, often keen sense of what is objective, relative, and reciprocal in his relationships with things and people.

ANTINOMY

In every neurosis we have to consider two well-defined ego systems; their modes and functions are quite contradictory. If, for instance, one system functions in the presence of the phobogenic object, this is enough to exclude the other system. If the logical system were not inhibited or abolished by fear, there would be neither phobia nor neurosis.

The phenomenon of antinomy is the source of inevitable conflicts between the two opposed systems. These conflicts give rise to a number of strange feelings and doubts, often unpleasant and disturbing, but at times ecstatic. These ideo-affective reactions are due sometimes to the patient's intuition, at other times to his clear perception of the fundamental conflict within his ego.

Examples of these are the feelings of being in disagreement with oneself or one's milieu; the feeling of incompleteness (the "incompletude" of Janet), of maladjustment, of unfulfillment, discontinuity, incoherence; feelings of failure, inadequacy, incapacity and inferiority.

This idea could be further applied to Janet's theories in order to expand them. Janet, that eminent specialist of the neurotic ego, has beautifully described all the symptoms we have just mentioned. But his concept of "lowering of psychic tension," which dominated all his theories, is in many cases not the cause but the effect of traumas and repeated conflicts between the two systems in question. Intermittent or chronic depression (psychasthenia) can follow these repeated conflicts.

The phenomenon of antinomy which is at the center of the symptomatology of the neurosis could thus serve as a connecting link between the Freudian and the nonanalytic theories and perhaps could reconcile them.

27. THE PRELOGICAL SECTOR AND THE NEUROSIS OF ABANDONMENT

There is one regressed sector with a different structure. The phobogenic object forms, so to speak, the "magnetic pole" of the phobic sector. Anxiety, originating in the subject, goes from the subject to the object, but in a double movement, returns to the subject as if it were emanating from the object. This return to the subject is due to the reversal of the affect into its reciprocal.

In the clinical entity I have termed the neurosis of abandonment, the regressed sector is subjected to an important structural modification while its basic nature remains unchanged. The magnetic pole is no longer an animal or a material object, but a living human being. Anxiety is objectified not in a cosmic image but in a human image.

But is it a pure image? It is the image of a real person, endowed with high prestige and great value. We call him an "authority object." This authority object has the power of creating or abolishing abandonment. He is all-powerful in this realm and thus, at times, benevolent, at times, malevolent. This first quality, the possibility of being at times benevolent, is inestimably valuable and distinguishes the authority object from the material phobogenic object. The latter produces only fear and insecurity. In contrast, the patient expects his authority object to create a better order of things in which confidence, joy, and happiness reign subjectively and objectively. This happy state is the concrete goal which the patient sets for the authority object's benevolent powers; these powers consist in arousing and maintaining the feeling of security and re-establishing it when it crumbles.

However, if the authority object fulfills his role badly or fails his duty through inadequate actions or psychological errors, he produces the reverse effects. To the subject, then deprived of his sure support, the object becomes a threatening figure to whom the subject, feeling cheated, attributes hostile feelings and intentions. The harm done by this regression consists in his giving the positive affect its corresponding and completive negative affect. To the abandoned patient, his suffering is always due to wickedness, not his own, of course, but that of the object who has failed him.

This theme of the double function of the object will be developed in Part III of this book. I only wish to point to an interesting phenomenon inherent in the neurosis of abandonment; this is the immense and vital role which a human being, similar to all others, can play in the life of another adult. It reminds one of the role of the mother for the child.

The authority object owes his vital importance not to himself but to the clinical condition of the subject. As with the phobic patient, this condition is a regression, or sometimes a fixation, to the initial prelogical level of affective relationships. The selective character of this regression is as marked as in the case of phobias. Here the regressed sector is defined by the sum of the ideo-affective phenomena pertaining to the authority object, directly or indirectly. The sector remains strictly limited to this relationship. Affective prelogic is manifested only in relation to the existence and the reactions of the authority object.

We understand why the subject relates so closely and attaches himself to such a person endowed with such supreme powers. Through his intervention, this unique being has the power to create and, through his lasting influence, to develop the precious feelings of valorization and security. We understand why an affective relationship based on such a benevolent action is the only one that can interest a person unable to achieve inner security and self-esteem. These feelings are indeed the indispensable factors for the functional equilibrium of the ego and for mental health.

However, when the subject attributes hostile feelings to the person who has failed him, he can then become most aggressive and try to vindicate himself. When he becomes aggressive, the vindictive subject has regressed to an infantile level. He feels and acts like a deceived child. To him insecurity and dissatisfaction are identical. At the source of his aggression we find a prelogical concept: the authority object has failed to acknowledge the vital value of an instinctual wish and failed to admit the legitimacy of an affective demand. The right to the need for security is unalienable, and the authority object is asked to satisfy this need fully.

From this it appears clearly that insecurity is equated with dissatisfaction and dissatisfaction confused with frustration. The vindictiveness implies the demand for fair amends.[2]

REGRESSION AND PROGRESSION

On the other hand, the same patient with his complex of abandonment is quite able to obey the laws and principles of the

[2] Cf. *Les deux sources conscientes et inconscientes de la vie morale.* 2nd ed., p. 173.

logic of relationships in all his contacts with persons who play no part in the maintenance of his feeling of security and the satisfaction of his need for love. With these people he behaves like an adult. His regressed sector being inactive, he is able to go about his business just as everyone else and just as well.

Here again we have the phenomenon of the functional duality of the ego, which is a structural duality. The function depends upon the structure.

Summary. In every clear-cut neurosis, two structures exist in the ego, and each sector is in opposition with the other. We have, then, two antinomic systems of unequal value and extent, whose laws conflict with each other and cannot be coordinated. They correspond to two very distinct stages of mental evolution. Their differences and divergences account for numerous neurotic symptoms, for much bizarre and inconsistent behavior which common sense unjustly condemns in patients with emotional illnesses.

The concept of structural duality seems to me to fill a gap in the understanding and the usual definition of adult psychoneurosis. A psychoneurosis consists of the presence and action of unconscious complexes to which is added an antinomy at the level of the ego. These two groups of morbid phenomena are related to each other but nevertheless distinct. In psychotherapy, it is important to analyze first each group as such, with its characteristic nature and functions, and only later treat one as a function of the other. In their genesis as well as in their pathogenic value, they are too different to be confused.

The progressive or "adaptive" sector remains subject to the rules of rational and affective logic, whereas the regressed sector is subject to the rules of prelogic.

28. The Fundamental Realistic Structure of the Neurosis of Insecurity

In all cases where the feeling of security is severely and permanently damaged, infantile realism is expressed by various means of an ideo-affective nature. One of these can be considered fundamental.

The subject spontaneously and without any investigation relates the modifications of his ego (or of some ego states) to an external cause. When these changes of the ego affect his feeling of security and valorization and thus the exercise of his ego functions, they are attributed without hesitation to the influence, be it positive or negative, of others, and especially of a certain authority object. The supposedly decisive action of this influence leads the subject to endow his object with magical powers and exceptional strength; this investment, or better, the reality of the invested attributes is later justified by their influence on the subject.

The person does not question the subjective factors of the process or the internal mechanisms which might be operating. He is blind to the fact that these subjective factors originate in his own mind and that the internal mechanisms partake of his own affectivity. The realism of the process escapes him completely as well as its infantile character.

In the last analysis, three closely related reasons oblige him to assume that the powers and influence of his object are magical: (1) The nearly reflex character of the investment; (2) the total absence of any search for psychological explanations or of self-analysis; (3) the unconscious nature of the subjective mechanisms and real causes of all his reactions.

The original situation of the child is here reproduced in all its details. The subject is aware only of his reactions, of which he can become conscious only as he functions in relation to his object, that is, in relation to a human element of the external reality.

29. The Relation between Neurotic and Infantile Thinking

A symptom is a phenomenon revealing a disturbance. In the neurotic patterns examined here, this disturbance has to become manifest in some conscious way to the subject. If the subject is not always aware of the pathological character of his disturbance, those in his environment soon notice it. The disturbance is bound to be expressed in the thought, affectivity, or behavior of the patient. A disturbance not evidenced by anything is not psychopathological.

To be expressed, a disturbance necessarily needs to adopt a form and have at its disposal a mental structure. Form and structure, however, are not to be found in the unconscious or in repressed tendencies but in the ego. It is the ego that determines the form and structure of a given symptom.

The content of the repressed elements has been crystallized in its infantile state. Thrust aside from the current of psychic life, these elements have escaped evolution, have not participated in the formation of the mind. Rudimentary and crude drives they were and so remain. Roughly speaking, they can be divided into two affective categories: desires and fears. These have retained their unique primitive objects and aims. These affects are, so to speak, immutable so long as the ego does not elaborate them into a symptom, does not transform them into an actual psychological process.

On the other hand, repressed elements are characterized by their latent or manifest dynamism, the very force which kept them alive. Richness in energy on one hand, psychological poverty on the other, is perhaps the best description of repressed drives. This poverty is in striking contrast to the richness and the infinite variations of neurotic symptomatology.

This infinite variety is due to the variety of the patient's individualities. However, the regressive mechanisms put into action by the ego are very much alike: in many symptoms, the ego is required to put magic thinking at the disposal of repressed fears or repressed wishes. The magical modes change little and give the variety of symptoms a certain monotony. As it deepens, regression levels individuality by lowering it to the infantile condition.

The part of the ego utilized by the unconscious complexes is the regressed sector which remains more or less under the influence of the unconscious. This functional relationship is an important fact which will be further studied in Section 35.

What remains to be examined now is why the regressed sector originated in the unconscious and remains linked to it, without consciousness entering the process.

30. PRIMITIVE AFFECTS AND MODES OF THINKING

The elaboration of neurotic symptoms is the work of the ego; the ego builds up the neurosis. Its materials are heterogenous and are provided by reality, the superego and the unconscious, as well as by elements of the ego. The latter elements help the ego to fill the gaps left by prelogical thinking. The various ways in which our patients try to explain to themselves and others their reactions, behavior, states of mind, their strange and sometimes apparently rational motivations are all secondary.[3] These reasons are the patients' efforts to re-establish a certain continuity in their lives and to introduce a certain logic into the prelogic used

[3] Freud called this process "rationalization." Cf. *Les deux sources conscientes et inconscientes de la vie morale*, 2d ed., p. 59. In the special sense given in this study, rationalization should not be understood in terms of reason or as a rational form, but signifies the act of putting logical thinking in the service of prelogical thinking.

on the neurotic level and used excessively during their phases of regression. During these phases, their reasoning is irrational, but the patients are usually unaware of it. Only when they recover do they realize the gaps in their thinking and the errors of their reasoning.

Evolved thinking, then, tends to establish a kind of compromise between the two antithetic systems; more exactly, it tries to reconcile the various ways in which the neurotic patient attempts to explain things and phenomena when primitive affects (fears, anxiety, etc.) have made him regress; and they produce his ways of explaining the same things when he is progressing and reasons more healthily. In the last analysis, all depends on the determining influences which these affects have or do not have upon his thinking, reason, and judgment.

THREE EXAMPLES

A good example is the rationalizations and rigid justifications of the patient with cancer phobia. He based them upon the incomplete and arbitrary character of certain medical methods and scientific theories. He reasoned that the real causes of cancer will always escape scientific research because they are related to the most intricate biological processes which, having presided over the creation of the organism, will also preside over its destruction. Going further, he refers to the concepts of the great philosophers who teach that we will never know all the laws that rule the relations between the universe and man, between objective reality and subjective phenomena.

Thus the patient postulates epistemological principles full of a radical relativism. On the other hand, in his prelogical explanations, his absolutism is just as radical. On the intellectual level, the "absolutes" of anxiety have contaminated thinking. Anxiety always imposes its absolutism on regressive thinking.

The superstitious person has similar arguments:

"If there are thirteen at a table—if I light three cigarettes on one match—well, I'm worried and can't concentrate. However, if I insist on only twelve, or refuse to light the third cigarette, then I feel reassured and I can think clearly again. Therefore these demands are legitimate and reasonable. They are logical and I am logical with myself."

"If I keep this ornament on my desk, always have on myself this fetish, then I am calm and work well. Anyway . . . one never knows what will happen. Therefore it is better for me to believe in these fetishes; it is safer to touch wood than not to."

Superstitious people base their reasoning upon a hedonic principle which in some ways is therapeutic: the principle of the suppression of suffering (the negative aspect of the pleasure principle). From the point of view of mental health this principle is defendable. (See Section 37 for the psychology of the superstitious person, and the "fearful type.")

Some persons are obsessed with verification. "Why do I have to make sure every night that the door or the gas jets are closed? Why do I have to do this three, seven or eleven times? It is very simple. I know . . . and pay for knowing it . . . that I am terribly absent-minded, incapable of concentrating on what I am doing. It would be very foolish not to verify these things. To neglect them could have severe consequences not only for myself but also for my family."

At the basis of this neurotic rationalization is a certain confusion between effects and causes. The patient says: my fear is due to my absent-mindedness. We tell him: your absent-mindedness is due to a deep-seated fear. You verify eleven times not because you are absent-minded or distracted but because you are anxious.

These obsessions recall a familiar structure, the primitive fear of the malevolent world and its deadly attacks. In the case quoted, the fear is objectified in the same way as with many children, and at the same time as with children, at the most critical moment of daily life, the evening, when night comes and dangers threaten everywhere. For the patient, the malevolent forces are concretized in the gas and its lethal power (asphyxia) or are incarnated in burglars and nocturnal murderers.

After every verification, doubt arises again; this is the essential factor in the problem that affect poses to thought. Doubt returns because anxiety is aroused again. Anxiety recurs despite verification. This revival of overpowering anxiety demonstrates to us that for the patient the feared accident is imminent, the anticipated misfortune is happening. The gas jet is open; asphyxia is starting; the door is unlocked; murderers will enter tonight.

In general, the obsession for verification can be traced back to serious traumas.

Summary. These prelogical explanations or attempts at rationalization always betray a relative but constant degree of thought's subservience to affect.

There are three forms of relationship between thought and primitive fears:

1. Thought is completely dominated by affect; it obeys affect through regression. Its explanations are based on precausal and magical implications.

2. Thought attempts to free itself from the influence of affect. As it does not succeed, it remains partially under this influence. Thought makes concessions to anxiety, attempts compromises which will be condemned by reason when better days come. The better days are phases of progression. This is the first degree of liberation when the subject tries to introduce logical elements into his spontaneous, magical and prelogical explanations.

3. The goal of the obsession for verification is clear. The patient wishes to go to bed with a feeling of security sufficient to warrant sleep. Generally, all of these kinds of symptoms have the same function of increasing security. If they accomplish their function well, thought can be entirely liberated from affect. Having slept well, the subject recuperates his faculties and can go about his work and pleasures normally. The ego faculties have recovered the conditions necessary for their normal exercise. Diurnal and rational thinking triumphs over nocturnal and irrational thinking until the latter, in the evening, will be predominant again.

A COMMENT ON FREUD, JANET AND THE CONCEPT OF REGRESSION

Freud has often insisted on always underscoring the active part played by the ego[4] in "symptom formation." For his part, Janet has given us rich and colorful descriptions of disturbances of ego life (hierarchy of tendencies, hegemony of inferior tendencies, etc.)

However, as far as I know, neither one has linked the psychopathology of the adult to the psychology of the normal child. Freud, for instance, did not refer to the close tie between the thinking of the obsessed patient, which is a pathological phenomenon, and magic thinking of the child, which is a normal developmental stage. An obvious bond links these two orders of phenomena, even though the first is pathological and the second is not. It is this very bond which defines the concept of regression and justifies its application to the analysis of neurosis.

[4] Freud has shown in convincing terms the systematic intervention of magic thinking in the malevolent or benevolent modes in the formation of obsessions and obsessive superstitions. I believe he was the first to show that the obsessional neurosis is founded on magic or on magical beliefs originating in childhood. He has also stressed the phenomenon of regression which he defines as the substitution of thought for action.

My clinical conclusion is the following. In no case of neurosis are the manifestations of structural duality entirely absent. Such an absence would mean the absence of a neurosis, and thus the presence of structural unity of the ego.

31. EXAMPLES OF THE EGO'S STRUCTURAL DUALITY

As I have mentioned, the regressed sectors characteristic of phobias and the neurosis of abandonment can be observed directly. They are projected into space, organized as functions of visible elements of the external reality. Everyone can note their existence and verify their prelogical modes. But in many patients this organization is not so obvious. The most alert mind cannot discover at once the secrets and solutions of these kinds of problems. Long study is often necessary and the patient usually requires psychoanalysis. I will give some examples chosen at random.

A. DISSOCIATION OF PATIENTS IN ANALYSIS

The following is a typical case of dissociation which rarely fails to occur during analysis. For this patient life is split into two sections, his analysis on one hand, and all the rest on the other. The wall between the two areas has absolutely no gaps. During the analytic sessions, he regresses visibly and adopts increasingly infantile and prelogical attitudes toward the analyst. He attributes to him the role of the authority object in all spheres. He attaches himself to the doctor, fearing him and criticizing him at the same time. Primary realism is re-established on the intellectual, moral and affective level (this mechanism was termed *transference* by Freud). This relapse is accompanied by inferiority and guilt feelings. For the one hour, heteronomy reigns.

However, after this brief and, in a way, artificial abdication, the length of which is determined in advance, autonomy and the logic of relationships regain their control. The analytic situation seems to produce the effect of a vaccination. It also has an undeniable therapeutic value.

B. THE REGRESSED MORAL SECTOR AND THE PROGRESSIVE INTELLECTUAL SECTOR

A professional and intellectual man harbors in himself two personalities in complete disagreement with each other.

1. In the sphere of moral and social behavior he suffers from a complete lack of personal opinions and judgments, betraying a strong feeling of inadequacy. He blindly and methodically defers to authority objects, such as teachers, superiors, rivals, his wife or his father. He is constantly watching for marks of approval or disapproval, sympathy or antipathy. He expects everything from an encouraging smile, fears everything from a frown. (This could be called the externalism of signs or a minor externalism.)

2. In professional and intellectual matters, he has personal and very determined opinions (mechanism of compensation). His judgments are subjected to objective examination and enlightened common sense. His attitudes are quite realistic; he is a good conversationalist and in discussions easily affirms his competency and defends his ideas, sometimes in heated arguments. In all questions pertaining to his profession or in problems of a general and philosophical nature of which he believes himself to have a well-rounded knowledge, he is "sure of himself" and can compete with anyone.

In short, in the first sector he is completely heteronomous, in the second, perfectly autonomous.

C. THE SUPERSTITIOUS GRADUATE

A very intelligent student is preparing for his final examinations in philosophy. Leaving his home for the oral examinations, he opens and closes the door to his room three times and touches the handle of the street door seven times. On his way, he pushes with his cane all unusual (malevolent) objects off the sidewalk. Reaching the university he repeats his regressed rituals, opens and closes the entrance door three times, then touches the handles of the door leading to the auditorium seven times. This done, everything has to turn out well. He swaggeringly enters the examination room, faces his examiners, and brilliantly answers their most difficult questions on psychology.

D. THE GENERAL AND THE HUSBAND

The following is the case of a general well known in military circles for his talents as a commander, his technical capacities, as well as his authority and energy. His subordinates tremble before him and respect him. But he trembles before his wife who is harsh, authoritarian and possessive. The contrast between the marital and martial sector is complete. As soon as his wife is in command, this officer loses his critical sense as well as his capacity for self-criticism.

E. THE BUSINESSMAN AND THE SON

This industrial magnate seems completely normal and very capable; his life and business are well organized. In social life he shows intelligence and logic, in family life, authority. He is successful, appreciated, envied; he is his own master.

However, he regresses completely in one area, the area of his relationship with his father. This terrifying father has remained for the patient the typical authority object. Before this man who has retained his absolute powers, the son becomes "a little boy" again and behaves like a fearful and obedient child. He cannot think of any other attitude except the "one-sided respect," so well described by Piaget. The principle of equal rights between two adults is neither understood nor accepted. For months, this patient used to say: "A father is always a father."

This obstinate affirmation implies the whole philosophy to which the child adheres without knowing it. Paternal authority is unconditional and independent of time. Even as an adult, the son remains a child. Even though he is the father of several children, in his parents' house, where he goes every day, he becomes again that which he has never ceased to be in their eyes: their child. In the patient's eyes, his father has remained the supreme being. When with him he easily changes from fear to rebellion, but so illogically that in the end he is always wrong and his father always right. Something is lacking. Only during the first ten years of a child's life does paternal authority proceed from a natural and inalienable right. However, this genetic principle is, even today, completely foreign to the patient, even though he himself has a family. He thus lives in complete contradiction with himself. With his father the authority principle is irreversible; not so with his own eldest son. On the contrary, with the latter he often tends to reverse the relation; he favors the autonomy of his own child and thus obeys the principle which he endlessly repeats to himself: "Above all, do not imitate your own father, do not weigh down your son."

What he lacks is the knowledge of what the logic of relationships between two adults should be. Far from being detrimental to filial respect, it only puts it on a healthy and fair basis. In this patient we see the son and the man. The son abolishes the fundamental principles of the logic of relationships; the man applies these same principles correctly and appreciates their value. The structural duality to which his behavior conforms is so gross that it disturbs his wife who in vain tells him: "So he *is* your father, all right, *but* . . ."

Self-criticism and the superego

Thus, in intelligent and sensible men (examples D and E), we can find a basic contradiction between a first way of behavior toward other people and a second way of behavior toward authority objects. The patients are often the only ones not to notice this gross discrepancy in themselves. These two examples well illustrate the most characteristic feature of this category of selective and momentary regression: the loss of self-criticism. With the officer, self-criticism is abolished in front of his wife (mother substitute); the businessman loses it in front of his father. Losing the faculty of self-criticism, they lose the capacity to criticize their authority objects. The two losses go together. In the absence of wife or father, and of any relationship with these two supreme beings, our two patients recover the use of these two faculties, use them freely, often too freely as a compensation. Nothing is more invigorating than to be able to put oneself in a place of authority without risking anything.

Before these persons of prestige, the ego cannot retain its identity. It is as if the regressed sector, invading the totality of the ego, replaces the ego and silences all its functions and faculties. Such sudden inhibitions are frequent in fearful children who are brought up very strictly. In an adult, this unconditional submission indicates a sort of mystical concept of parental authority which leads to abdication of the will and loss of the liberty of opinion, in one word, of autonomy, on the altars of that blindly venerated Being "who is always right."

Genetically, the two concepts of infantile superego and lack of self-criticism are always related. This relation is logical. The infantile superego is a kind of historical monument in the midst of a modern city, a witness to the time when realistic heteronomy in the child was due to his incapacity to evaluate his idea-feelings, criticize his own judgments, and trace back his reasonings. In short, the child is incapable of examining his own heteronomy critically for the simple reason that he is not aware of it; the idea of heteronomy escapes him necessarily because the idea of autonomy is still foreign to him. In well-defined circumstances, the officer and the businessman are still in this stage. Self-criticism depends on the autonomy of the mind. The paradox is that one has to be autonomous in order to realize that one is or is not any more.

F. PROJECTION OF THE COMPLEMENT OF GUILT FEELING

Here is a final and typical example occurring in certain individuals who are obsessed by the fear of displeasing, being disliked, or receiving criticisms and blows. They constantly dread being lectured to or told what people think of them. They go about walking on eggs, apologizing for everything they do. In any unfavorable situation, they regress to externalism. The factors in this regression are guilt feelings whose strength is due to repressed drives. At the source of their chronic fear is a mechanism mentioned frequently in this work. These subjects objectivate the "complement of their affect," that is, the affect due to guilt.

As I have already shown, there is logic even in prelogic: the logic of a child. If he has been burned, bitten by a dog, or if mother has "left him all alone" and unfortunately at this moment his conscience is not quite at ease, the child considers these misfortunes to be punishments for his disobediences and misdeeds. This is the way he sees things as long as moral realism constitutes his only mode of thinking and reacting.

This mode has left its marks on the ego of patients suffering from the obsession of being criticized. What is more natural than to expect to be abused, punished or persecuted, when the conscience is burdened by small and large remorses. Nothing then is more logical than to think that one inspires antipathy, ill-will, or even hate. In the moral neurosis, the complement of guilt is always aggression from others, and especially from an authority object.

32. Ignorance of the Principle of Reversibility Resistance to the Transposition of Judgments

We can now consider two very different types of relationships or positions of criticisms, depending on whether (1) the subject (S) has to judge and estimate another person (O) considered as "a being per se," and different in essence from S; this we will call position A. Or (2) whether S is, or believes himself to be, the object of judgment and appreciation by others, or believes that he has to judge and estimate himself; this is position B. The principles applied in position A and those in position B are in complete opposition to each other and irreversible.

G. SUPEREGO AND SELF-DEPRECIATION

Let us examine these relationships more closely by describing a case. In this case O is the patient's colleague and friend and is not afraid to affirm his personality and defend his intellectual autonomy. He defends his opinion with good arguments, and it is evident that he attributes value to his ideas. S is incapable of this. How could be valorize his ideas before he has acquired any self-value?

In the presence of O or in discussions with him, S feels ill at ease; he has doubts about himself. These doubts paralyze him and induce him to transform his friend into an authority object whose prestige lasts as long as the discussion. Naturally the discussions always turn into monologues.

S gives reasons for his lack of ease. "I am horribly afraid of being unpleasant, averse, presumptuous, ridiculous, etc." If one goes beyond these affirmations, one discovers the real reasons for these exaggerated fears. Above all S fears to be wrong, and that O will discover his errors. To be so judged would overwhelm him with confusion.

Psychogenetic analysis reveals the source of this externalistic reaction. The reaction proceeds from a confusion frequent in childhood but from which an intelligent adult should be free: the confusion between error and fault. S has not yet learned to distinguish between them. He puts morality where it does not belong and persists in viewing error or omission as the result of a sin of the mind. To him knowledge is a virtue, ignorance an unpardonable sin.

To escape from his uneasiness, S has two ways out: he can affirm himself but that means exposing himself to criticism which in itself is considered as terrible, or he can give in and assume that O is right in all matters and always. "If I were to contradict him, he would have a bad opinion of me. I would lose his esteem and sympathy . . . If he speaks about something, he knows about it. If I gave another opinion, I would, in his eyes, seem to have a too high opinion of myself. He would rightly think me conceited or a fool. Maybe he would not say it openly. But between what people tell you and what they really think about you and never tell you . . . is all the difference between frankness and politeness . . ."

In essence, I reply, "Your statements obviously presuppose two categorical postulates. One: that O is always right and never errs. Two: that you a priori endow him with the absolute right to judge you or contradict you; whereas you deny yourself the same right. What do you make of the principles of relativity and reciprocity? For you, there are two weights and two measures. You simultaneously apply two contradictory laws, depending on whether you judge O or you think that he judges you. You must learn that the contrary of doubt is not assurance and rigid affirmation but independence."

During another session he starts again on the same theme, but viewed in a more general aspect. If someone else makes an error, it is not a fault. If someone else suffers a defeat, it is bad luck, chance, fate, "the roof fell on his head." And he adds, "I feel very sorry for him." However, this law of indulgence does not work for himself. For him there is only one rigorously strict rule: "To judge oneself without indulgence is good, humble, Christian. Above all, it is less dangerous." Truly, nothing mimics humility better than an inferiority complex. "If I abandon this principle what will I do? I could seek excuses for my errors and faults and certainly would find excellent ones. However, where does one stop? In the end, I will inevitably come to think a great deal of myself and I hate such a vice . . . No, this would be wrong and dangerous. To pretend that I am superior to myself, would endanger what I am. To judge others is to put oneself above them, to look down on them. It is to reverse the scale; I don't think I have the right to do it—or the courage. And—then one becomes disillusioned—and has to pay for it—etc."

This is a third right which he denies himself and liberally accords to others, as if his generosity could afford him some relief. This right is the right for excuses. In principle, others may always have some excuses, he never. This principle is the one of limited responsibility which the courts apply when they consider the role of extenuating circumstances. Their verdicts thus are based upon a moral relativism, the psychological value and fairness of which can be appreciated by any evolved, mature person.

However, where the patient is concerned, responsibility is never diminished, culpability always complete. Inasmuch as no extenuating circumstances exist for a fault, and even error is a moral transgression, there can be no excuse for being wrong. The confusion of levels is as total as it is in childhood. But while normal in a child, this confusion is a severe symptom of regression in the adult. For a long time during his analysis, the patient could neither understand nor admit this anomaly. It is almost amusing that a man with a university degree should consider error as an intellectual sin.

Since his childhood, these conceptions had remained deeply engrained in this patient's mind. His parents did everything to maintain their son's conviction that a grave error is as reprehensible as a grave fault.

Limited responsibility for others, total responsibility for himself; two weights and two measures—and this intelligent man refused to see that he was unfair to himself. In this regressed sector, false morality supplants intelligence. The clouding of the faculty to judge is evident. Intact in the progressive sector, this faculty regains mature functioning as soon as impersonal problems are considered.

As a subject, my patient is always wrong; his object always right. But it is only in appearance that the patient condemns himself. In reality, externalism is the basis of his attitude. It is evident that it is impossible for him to pronounce a judgment on himself without the intervention of someone else's opinion either directly or indirectly. This person must be someone whom he considers vastly superior to himself, whom he even holds to be infallible. In the end, he devaluates himself exactly as much as he overvalues the authority object. This need to put oneself always on a lower level characterizes the neurosis with moral devaluation, which is based entirely on infantile realism that has developed and expanded into adult externalism. In short, this man is unable to judge his own value objectively. He never expects anything good and true from himself and can act only in conformity with what he thinks others expect from him.

In position B, he still is at the level of "unilateral respect" and has not yet reached the level of mutual respect.[5]

[5] In this note I will briefly outline some facts in this patient's life history. He was born and brought up in a truly Balzacian milieu, in an upper middle class home, in a French province. The educational technique of his parents was that no matter what they would do or not do, say or not say, confess or dissimulate, obey or disobey, their children were always suspect and, by definition, guilty. The parents, on the other hand, were infallible.

In this atmosphere of suspiciousness, as the powerless and anxious victim of

A series of interpretations and explanations of this kind brought the patient to a new kind of complaint which denoted a change in structure. "There are two individuals in me. The one is Me . . . poor soul. The other is 'He,' a sort of odious mentor who never misses a chance to preach and scold me. It is as if his only pleasure was to humiliate me and pin me down. 'Ah, Ah,' he tells me, 'you want to do this because you like it. Oh, no, you have to do that; you started this work which you are interested in . . . well, start this one which bores you and which you have neglected. Vain person that you are, you should have remained silent.' You should—you should—this is what I endlessly hear. Just wait, and you will see, it will come to a bad end . . . I tell you . . . remember it . . ." On the whole, Pascal should always do what he is not doing, be where he is not. After one month of treatment he grew bold and let loose his long repressed rebellion. "Look at this awful guy. I wish I could take him by his shoulders and shake him until he gives in. To silence him I have only one

---

so many injustices, the child gave way to legitimate acts of protest and revolt. Then the atmosphere would become venomous.

There was never a week when Pascal did not have to ask forgiveness on his knees. He resisted, his throat tightened, then he would curtly say the words. His lack of sincerity and contrition only aggravated his problem. He always had to atone for his next sin. The initial misdeed was forgotten, only the sin of insolence counted, and thus a whole chain of reactions was set in motion. The present fault evokes the memory of the last one, which evokes the one before that, and so on until the first that his judges have not forgotten is reached. With every misdeed the same thing happened with the recounting of the ever-increasing load of sins—all of which Pascal found grossly unfair. From these crushing and almost liturgic scenes, the sinner, despite himself, never emerged forgiven and white-washed. On the contrary, every time the load was heavier with a new sin. No technique could have been better suited to develop irremediable feelings of guilt and unworthiness in this child. These were the essential materials Pascal had at his disposition to build and organize his superego.

Today, Pascal is a man. However his parents are reincarnated in the implacable and infallible authority object. The child reappears in the adult with his unshakable conviction of guilt. The idea of pardon and forgiveness, of possible innocence, are foreign to him. He has remained at the stage of "objective responsibility" analyzed by Piaget (*The Moral Judgment of the Child*, Chapter II).

means: yell louder and tell him off, 'That's enough, shut up, leave me in peace'." From then on the atmosphere of the analysis was different.

Interestingly the subject, though knowing that in reality his accuser is inside himself, expressed himself as if the accuser were external, incarnated in a strange and hateful person. This persecutor is, so to speak, the external agent of the process of self-depreciation and devaluation which takes place in the ego. When an authority is thus the speaker for the infantile superego through projection, the subjective fears and remorses are given an increased reality, truth, and strength. In his new attitude, Pascal is half-way between externalism and interiorization. He is in the process of becoming conscious of the parental superego within himself and in so doing of its existence, its actual psychological function and its genesis. Thus he proceeds toward a cure which will consist in the elimination of the regressed sector. But before it can be eliminated, it has to become conscious; then it is necessary to change its structure by modeling it along the lines of the structure of the progressive sector.

This case is also interesting from another viewpoint. It illustrates the relationship between the infantile superego on one hand, and the moral life and behavior on the other. In Pascal the relation is clear; the parental superego, retaining its primitive form, has kept the realm of morality under its influence and domination. This influence prevented the formation of an autonomous moral conscience and the simultaneous development of what I call moral intelligence and Piaget calls "the intelligence of the logic of interindividual relationships." In this respect, Pascal has been engulfed in an evident and fatal state of "moral stupidity." His accuser is but the living voice of his parents and the persisting echo of the humiliating scenes to which he was subjected in childhood.

33. The Test of Reversibility

One day I suggested to Pascal a little experiment of applied logic. "You impute to your friend qualities which are as flattering as they are hazardous; you allow him liberties which go beyond those of the human condition. But you also attribute to him rather doubtful powers, such as divine omniscience and wisdom. In a word, you call him infallible and then you accuse him of taking advantage of his superhuman priviliges.

"Well, for a moment exchange places with him. You are your friend and thus must declare yourself to be all-knowing, infallible, and make a false god of yourself. At the same time you consider your friend ignorant and stupid. Being thus in his place, what would you think of such pretention and vanity? What would your judgment of yourself be?" "Oh, that is very simple, I would hold myself the worst kind of idiot—or a grandiose madman—It is clear; I never thought of it."

We see that the principle of reciprocity is foreign to him. That is why he overvalues his supposed judges and humiliates himself. He is incapable of putting himself in the place of others and vice versa. The roles are irreversible. This belief in two opposite laws, in the rule of two weights and measures, a big measure for others, a very small one for himself, are enough to demonstrate his faliure in an essential and logical mental operation: the unification of principles and criteria.

COMMENT

Position B (S is the object of judgment by others or himself) is based upon prelogic. Irreversibility precludes reciprocity. If a person completely condemns his own morality, while completely approving that of others, there is no relativity. If one attributes to others one's own system of judgment, there is no objectivity.

Position A (S judges others), on the contrary, is built on a logical basis so long as S is not personally involved. If this condition is fulfilled, he judges people, events and things healthily. He judges others and analyzes their interrelationships according to the principles of the logic of relationships.

Since there is regression in one case and adaptation in the other, two structural sectors are involved; there is a duality of the ego. What is right for others is wrong for the subject and vice versa.

Here is another example. Bertha is a young girl living in modest circumstances. She works hard all day and comes home in the evening exhausted and sleepy. However, living with her widowed mother, she feels obliged to stay up with her during the evening. The mother can hardly hide her pleasure at having her daughter's company as long as possible. My patient says bitterly, "I need sleep so much, have to get up so early and go to bed late. . . But what can I do? I do it out of consideration for my poor mother. I really cannot leave her alone in the evenings. If by chance I go to bed early, she does not say anything . . . but she sighs sadly . . . and I know what these sighs mean. They are like reproaches. But, of course, she is perfectly right in her loneliness to demand these sacrifices of me. It is only fair." Bertha is unbending on this point.

I say, "But suppose you are the mother of a hardworking girl. You do nothing all day long; in the evening you demand from your daughter, more or less openly, that she keep you company despite her extreme fatigue. How would you judge these demands?" "Well," Bertha replied uneasily, "I think they are unworthy of a mother. But with my mother, it is different. Your supposition is absurd. . ."

This patient had lost her father before puberty. He seems to have been a remarkable man. As a child, the patient loved him deeply. His premature death was a terrible blow. Even now she has not recovered from this trauma. Her submissive attitude toward her mother is an indirect proof of this. When Bertha was led to her father's coffin, like a bolt of lightning a wish-idea passed through her mind: "If only mother were dead instead of father." This wish was immediately repressed in an attempt to relieve the strong guilt feeling attached to it. Relegated to the unconscious, this remorse from then on disturbed the activity of one important ego sector in which the image of the mother-judge was central. At present, this remorse exerts its influence whenever the girl is with her mother. The latter cannot be subjected to any criticism, any depreciatory judgment; she is "taboo." The "maternal sector" is dominated by the same moral realism which ruled at the time when Bertha, under the influence of a crushing trauma, desired her mother's death.

When I suggested to the patient that she reverse viewpoints, I was probing for her latent aggressiveness. I had set a kind of trap into which she promptly fell, tempting her to express her repressed resentment and accumulated grievances. In judging herself an "unworthy mother"—in a very violent and implacable tone of voice—she condemned her own egocentric and tyrannical mother.

This reversal entailed the danger of a psychological accident that could have disrupted the moral and affective balance of my patient. To blame poor mother, to get angry at her, to want to get rid of her with all her demands, might arouse in the patient feelings that "she is not wanted . . . that another—the father—should be in her place, etc." Under the mounting pressure of her unacknowledged and repressed wishes, Bertha might have lost all control of herself. She had to remain calm, affable, affectionate so that no word, no gesture would be able to revive the death wishes and thus betray her unconscious desires.

Recovering their original strength, these wishes might have brought about a definite separation, that is, a symbolic satisfaction; and under the influence of her moral conscience, Bertha could never do this or she would have had to judge herself an "unworthy daughter."

In summary, Bertha's excessive indulgence toward her mother and her no less excessive severity against herself are two simultaneous and related phenomena which are explained by her adherence to a moral system existing at the time when the forbidden wish was repressed. With her mother, Bertha always felt herself to be wrong and always sided with her "poor mother" even when the latter prevented her from getting her well-deserved rest and sleep. This attitude toward the mother was irreversible.

Filial Love and Regression

Because of Bertha's childhood adoration of her father, it was natural that she should see him as perfect and infallible. Over-valuation accompanies oedipal love. At the age of twenty-six, however, it is not natural that she should still see him so; yet this was the case without her being aware of it. Very simply, her father remained to her as he was when she lost him: the eminently benevolent being.

"Let us suppose," I said to her, "that you would have been spared this terrible grief. Your father is alive and claims that he is perfect and infallible. He flatters himself with knowing everything. What would you think of him?" Silence, uneasiness, anger. Then sharply, "One does not judge a loved dead one. His memory is sacred."

The patient thus confuses filial love and regression to realism, and her indignation shows that I had touched upon a second taboo. The paternal taboo is prescribed by love; the maternal taboo is imposed by the superego as a defense against unconscious hate. In contrast, toward all other people, Bertha's judgment is autonomous and correct. Freed from all intellectual and moral realism, it is grounded upon a healthy reciprocity. The hostility theme against the mother, considered in the past as the child's rival, was approximately this: the girl resented that her rival had survived her beloved father and thus had usurped his rights, his powers, and his place; of course, these grievances and reproaches remained unconscious. Such hostility toward the mother with the love for the father as a counterpart is obviously of oedipal origin.

This is again an example of the projection of the complement of guilt. As we have already said, the completive attribute of hate is blame and severity with the self, even harshness when the object of hate is a person such as an unhappy mother whom one is supposed to respect, love and honor. Repressed hatred compels the subject to attribute to the authority object malevolent intentions and plans for severe punishment. Thus Bertha's mother has the right to make the most revolting and least maternal demands. The punishment in this case is the lack of sleep and the subsequent neurotic symptoms.

Again a genetic law is verified, the law that every projection is followed by irreversibility. The subject becomes blind to the logic of relationships and remains so as long as the mechanisms of objectification of the affect remains unconscious. "If I behaved like mother, I would be unworthy and hateful. But behaving as she does, mother is all the more worthy and likable."

CHAPTER FIVE

ATTEMPT AT CLASSIFICATION OF NEUROTIC SYMPTOMS

REPRESSION AND REGRESSED SECTOR

34. The Three Types of Neurotic Symptoms

Numerous combined analyses of the most varied cases have led me to distinguish three types of neurotic symptoms depending on the form and the degree of ego intervention. In this description we will start with the lowest degrees of ego intervention and proceed to the higher ones.

1. Symptoms where the ego is least active: where the symptoms, so to speak, occur despite the ego, for example, sexual impotency and frigidity.

Eventually, the ego always reacts to every symptom, even if it has not directly participated in its creation. Often the secondary reactions finally dominate the clinical picture, whereas the physical symptoms of nervous origin are relegated to the background. Among the secondary reactions are affective impotency, lack of virility, incapacity to love, lack of interest in all kinds of pleasures, all the various disappointments and failures resulting from sexual impotency, and the magic thinking processes started by anxiety attacks.

For example there is the phenomenon of the breakdown of the ego defenses when the ego is suddenly invaded, paralyzed and dominated by an unconscious impulse, such as a sudden sadistic or masochistic act or a sudden and unmotivated revolt against authority. In these cases, the drive is manifested and realized just as it is. The ego has neither time nor the power to elaborate on it, to use reactions of flight or defense. This break-through of drives is due to the dynamic power of the repressed elements.

2. Symptoms which are the direct or indirect consequence of the antinomy that is created by the regression of one sector and the progressive evolution of another sector. Here we deal with a more or less clear awareness of inner disagreement, discrepancy, lack of confidence, feelings of maladjustment to reality and social environment, with inadequate responses to problems and demands, and the constant recurrence of "the things which go wrong" related to relapses into infantile prelogic.

"I've quarreled with my father," says one patient. "I no longer get along with my wife," says another. And those in their environment note that: "He (or she) is again in one of his (or her) bad phases."

All these symptoms are, generally, the result of awareness of the irreducible antagonism between the two systems and the inhibition which is the product of this antagonism.

The most typical example in this group is the *moral neurosis;* it consists in a series of conflicts between the ego and the infantile superego, the latter being the typical regressed sector. The "scruple" arises at the border between ego and infantile superego. Dominated by self-doubts, the overscrupulous individual in his interminable meditations never arrives at a solution because the autonomous moral conscience and the infantile superego obey contradictory rules. Each paralyzes the other through their contradictions. Deferring to the antiquated principles born of moral realism, the infantile superego defeats the autonomous judgments of value issued by the moral conscience.[1]

From this point of view, the scruple, as well as all symptoms

[1] Cf. *Les deux sources conscientes et inconscientes de la vie morale,* 2nd. ed., p. 138.

belonging to this category, can be compared to "points of friction."

3. Symptoms due to the activity of the regressed sector itself. It is needless to recall that this activity can be due to true regression or to a fixation in realism and adualism. All the disturbances caused by externalism belong to this category.

Some of these symptoms are of special interest because they highlight the most original and the most intimate parts of the ego, the parts which really belong to it, for which it is responsible and which it regulates. These are the *feelings of valuation and security*. They are created and regulated by the ego. In certain types of neuroses, their function is inhibited by regression or abolished by fixation at an infantile stage. These disturbances characterize the group of neuroses with insecurity and self-devaluation.

This group of symptoms can be divided into three subgroups depending on the disturbance affected:

A. disturbances in the formation and the mode of regulation of these feelings;

B. disturbances in their stability and their duration;

C. disturbances in their quality, strength and value.

This body of disturbances characterizes a frequent form of neurosis known to the layman as the "inferiority complex" and, in my terminology, the "neurosis of insecurity and self-devaluation." The above-mentioned disturbances indicate the nature and the degree of gravity of this neurosis. At the present, I believe this neurosis to have assumed the character of an epidemic, typical of our times.

35. REPRESSION AND REGRESSED SECTOR. REMARKS ON PSYCHOGENESIS

I wish to mention at this point an interesting symptom without going into the more complex problems which it poses. I leave these to the psychiatrists who are particularly interested in this special aspect of neuroses.

Many times I have alluded to the uniquely human structure which since Freud we have called the superego. What is the superego? What is its origin? How is it formed and at what time in the mental evolution?

Its formation, as Freud discovered, takes place between the fifth and the tenth year. It is, according to Freud, the heritage of the oedipus complex. Its function is to inhibit the oedipal strivings, be they sexual (and incestuous) or aggressive. The sexual drives have as their object the parent of the opposite sex or parent substitute; the aggressive drives' object is the parent of the same sex.[2]

To this primary function of inhibition, a second is later added: the function of preventing the return of the repressed. It is a function of blocking and resistance.

Viewed from Freudian theory, the infantile superego is the result of the repression of instinctual drives in general, and the oedipal drives in particular; in short, the repression of all the drives prohibited and condemned by the child's educators. This is the dynamic aspect of the formation of this apparently moral structure.

Whenever the realistic attitudes of the child meet with the demands of education, the infantile superego never betrays its origin, more than that—it reaffirms them on every occasion which reminds the child of this origin. This "fidelity" to its origins constantly brings the infantile superego in contradiction and opposition with the autonomous moral conscience. This antagonism manifested on the level of behavior and ideals and born of the dual structure of the ego is quite capable of disturbing the social and affective life of an incompletely evolved individual.

[2] See Freud's *The Ego and the Id* and my analysis in *Les deux sources conscientes et inconscientes de la vie morale*, 2nd ed., p. 103.

But a new question arises. Why does this "intra-ego" structure, called the infantile superego, persist in applying the principles and rules of prelogical realism? For what reason does it maintain the principle of authority so absolutely and with so much power? In other words, why does the superego become a regressed sector and why does it maintain this position despite the formation of an autonomous moral conscience as a progressive sector? This is a fact not sufficiently clarified by Freud's explanations. We ask ourselves whether it was absolutely necessary that the superego should remain fixed in realism? The purely dynamic explanation of the phenomenon does not imply this.

This objection seems justified. The *dynamic character,* even the purely instinctive and affective activity of the superego, is not enough to explain its *psychological character.*

Generalizing, the same can be said of the phenomenon of repression. Like the superego, which is the most important consequence of repression, it has two aspects: a dynamic and a properly psychological one. The first has to do with the superego and defines its functions; the second has to do with the ego and defines the consequences of repression inside the ego. These consequences will later and for a long time disturb the ego's life and can be summarized in one sentence: the formation and persistence of a regressed sector.

Having posed this problem I will now leave it and return to the elucidation of three psychogenetic principles of more general value in psychopathology.

A. We are told that repression eliminates all contact between the ego and what has been repressed. This is too absolute an affirmation. Between the two, a zone survives which relates one to the other and which might be termed a "zone of contacts or relays." Because of this zone, the ego and the repressed remain in contact. This zone is part of the ego and its activity retains the imprint of realism. It is regressive in its mechanism of defense against the repressed drives as well as in the means by which, at the same time, it seeks to satisfy these very drives. Such means are the displacement of objects and goals of the repressed drives, the varied camouflages and disguises. Such activity recalls clearly the ambivalent attitude of the child toward authority. The child tries to obey but at the same time seeks appeasements and compensations for those needs and wishes which the parents disapprove and for which they punish him. He will then do it "behind their backs" which is enough to show to what extent he is dependent upon authority—demonstrating it in this manner as much as with his obedience. Revolt is as realistic as unconditioned submission. The subject conceives of autonomy only as opposed to heteronomy; he is not able to see its own value.

B. Repression has not one but two consequences: the first obviously consists in the resultant formation of the "repressed" and the second, in the formation of the contact zone on the level of the ego. The latter is characterized by infantile functional modes by virtue of its regressed structure.

C. The sector which remains in contact with the repressed remains fixed in its structure at the developmental stage reached by the individual at the time when repression took place. Freud proved that repression is at the source of adult neuroses and that the pathogenic repressions take place during childhood.

36. General Conclusions

There are some additional conclusions concerning the concept of the progressed sector. It would be wrong to define this sector in a negative sense, as if progressing simply meant not regressing. Progression can certainly be defined by itself, not only in relation to the inverse processes of regression. To advance means more than not to go back.

Let us consider the clearest and most striking example of

progression during adolescence. The positive progression accomplished during this period is characterized by two parallel and related processes: (1) the acquisition of more intellectual aptitudes, of rational thinking and its correct use, and of the body of ideas which are at the basis of the logic of relationships; (2) the development of the ego functions and their normal operations (see Introduction).

The aptitudes are the intellectual aspect of the progress of the mind. They define the quality of thought or of the "thinking personality." The ego functions are the more affective aspect of this progress. They define character and determine the individual's usual way of acting and reacting to his social environment. For young people who develop normally and mature healthily, it is a great accomplishment to acquire internal security and self-esteem during adolescence. However, this is insufficient. The third gain of autonomy is the final achievement. This "seventh stage" (see Introduction) is genetically the last and with it the peak of personality development may be reached.

Compared to this optimistic picture, the regressed sector strikes one with its negative characteristics. The neurotic symptoms which reveal the genesis and the nature of the activity in this sector can be divided into two groups:

Group I. This group includes about all the psychic functions of the infantile prelogical stage. In the adult, this infantilism, partial as it may be, is patently a pathological manifestation. This is the genetic aspect of the neurotic process which manifests itself in a factor characteristic of the ego of neurotics. But this process also has an aspect that I would call "present." It consists of all the disturbances currently experienced by our patients.

Group II. In the course of regressive phases, it is only rarely that depression does not occur. Regression and depression go together. This is a particular form of damage to the ego functions which I will analyze more closely in Part III of this book. The principal elements involved have been mentioned; they are the results and consequences of antinomy (see Section 26). Among them are the feelings of disagreement with oneself and with the milieu, and the feelings of insufficiency, inadequacy, insecurity and failure. These disturbances and others of the same kind, which will be examined later, constitute the third category in the general classification of neurotic symptoms proposed in Section 34. They affect the three ego functions of autonomy, valuation and security.

These three ego functions are in general more or less damaged in the regressed states causing depression or in depressive states causing regression. Like most other neurotic processes, regression is most often selective. It can seriously damage some function and leave others intact. In appearance, at least, this is true; in reality the damage in the end always affects the whole of ego life or the "body of functions" described in the Introduction.

The form and evolution of dysfunctional ego syndromes are related to this selective action which itself depends upon the genetic evolution of the individual. Logically we can conclude that there exist three clinical forms depending on which of the three essential functions is involved:

1. In the more common neurosis the patients present most frequently disturbances in their autonomy and its increasing diminution is characteristic of the evolution of these illnesses. They become more and more dominated by their unconscious and ruled by the infantile superego.

2. The function of self-valuation is especially disturbed in patients with inferiority complexes. The self-esteem is, so to speak, reversed and leads to the feeling of having no value. Such a feeling is not imagined but is a reality.

3. The function of the feeling of security is particularly damaged in the phobic neurosis and the neurosis of abandonment.

The evolution of a neurosis of the second and third type is characterized by alternating periods of regression and progression. Under unfavorable conditions (social, moral and affective), the patient relapses to the infantile level and rises again rapidly to affective equilibrium when the circumstances again become favorable. These vicissitudes give rise to painful feelings of lack of unity, of discontinuity within oneself. The patients have a clear intuition of this alternating play, although this inner awareness is but a powerless witness to it. Using similar images, they express themselves in almost identical words:

"You see, Doctor, I am tired of fighting with myself. I feel like two people, me and this other . . . It is as if I had two selves. When I am myself, I feel secure and can handle the situation. I feel well and all goes well . . . But when the other comes back, I am unsure of myself; I feel dominated by people and events and go from disappointment to disappointment . . ."

"Me, myself" stands for the progressive sector, the adult; the "other" is the regressed sector, the child.

CHAPTER SIX

TWO FUNDAMENTAL TYPES OF STRUCTURES

37. The Fearful and the Aggressive Types

These two types are often mentioned in medicopsychological publications. Physicians in their practice have ample opportunity to observe them. My aim is to attempt to relate them to two fundamental types of prelogical structures. Through psychogenetic principles, clinical facts are thus related to child psychology.

The Fearful Individual Who Escapes

At the basis of this syndrome is a natural, instinctive fear which is manifest or latent. If manifest, the fear takes hold of the ego and dominates consciousness. If latent, the fear remains buried in the unconscious, but is always ready to flare up during trying periods or danger or when confronted with the hostility of the world and the social milieu. The patient has never mastered this affect. When it is analyzed during a period of regression, we find that to the patient reality has retained all of its original malevolent character. The psychological basis of the symptoms is at the level of the anxiety of the weak confronted with the strong, of the powerless fighting the powerful. At this very early level, as I have mentioned before, the helpless child feels that his very life is threatened; later he feels that his security is threatened. Security then retains a vital psychic importance.

The powerful strength of primary anxiety is demonstrated by phobias and nightmares which reveal its potentialities. Even between crises, the patients remain fearful to the very depths of their beings. This fear is easily displaced onto society. But it also influences the characters of these persons, making them worried, timid, inhibited, without, however, damaging their aptitudes and talents. They are easily shocked and dismayed by reality which they can only understand by reference to their own affective reactions. Something of the fear of the big bad fire remains in them, as if fire had been invented just to burn them alive.

One has the impression that their first wounds never healed; they could never forget the offenses of the world and the betrayals of their protectors. Even if all parents would loyally promise to every newborn infant to fulfill their duties as benevolent beings, it would be practically impossible for them to keep these promises always and everywhere. Material obstacles inevitably arise every day between the protector and the protected. A normal child is not disturbed too much by this, but the fearful child has a tendency to confuse these fortuitous and inevitable obstacles with malevolent intentions. Everything that separates him from his mother is a source of danger and insecurity. His fears are always ready to rise again, and they tell us of his foremost need: security as engendered by his mother. To the child, she is bound to this through a law more categorical than moral law. The child would not hesitate to speak of "sacred duty" if he could have such a concept. At this age more than at any other, security means above all not to be deceived. We could define the enviable condition of the individual who has been spared deception by the Greek word *asphaleia*.[1]

[1] There is no simple term to designate this state. In Greek, *sphallo* means: to deceive, to induce error; *sphaleia* would be a word defining the state of one who has been deceived. On the other hand, *asphaleia* defines the inverse state of one who is not or has not been deceived. Interestingly enough, this word is usually translated as "security." The wise men of antiquity have thus placed deceit at the basis of insecurity. All children would confirm this without knowing Greek.

To create and develop *asphaleia* should be the only rule for parents and educators, and this is especially true when they are faced with a fearful child. To the child who sees them as all-knowing and all-powerful gods, it is incomprehensible that they should allow themselves so many faults and are so unable to keep their promises. To the child the state of *sphaleia* remains a cruel and unfathomable mystery, a mystery which adults suffering from phobias and the neurosis of abandonment are also incapable of solving.

A fearful child, instead of demanding, revendicating, and accusing when he has been deceived, withdraws and becomes silent. In some cases he sulks; in others he flees. He will hide himself; he will be found in the attic, up a tree or in a closet. Other children will "run away." Believing themselves to be abandoned, they abandon those who have disappointed them. To the child this is the only way to end abandonment. Such cases are usually handled through the courts and the child guidance agencies.

Comments on Superstitious People

Superstitious people constitute a subgroup of the fearful personality type; they have no proclivity to adopt the solutions of the phobic patients or the patients with the neurosis of abandonment, nor do they have any inclinations to resort to dramatic measures. In order to ward off the offenses of the world and of evil people, they simply invest certain objects or certain gestures with inverse, benevolent powers (positive magic or propitiatory magic).

The objects can be lucky pieces, talismans, charms and any of the fetishes. The doll or teddy-bear from which the infant never parts, especially when he goes to bed, are the classical prototypes of these objects.

ANXIETY AND
MAGIC THINKING

By CHARLES ODIER, M.D.

Translated by MARIE-LOUISE SCHOELLY, M.D.
and MARY JANE SHERFEY, M.D.

Anxiety and Magic Thinking represents one of the first attempts at an integration of psychoanalytic concepts with the findings of Piaget's genetic psychology. The author, a Swiss psychoanalyst, devotes several chapters to an examination of these two theories, and demonstrates their synthesis in a discussion of the concept of anxiety. He then proceeds to apply his ideas to clinical phenomena, first investigating the phobias. His novel approach leads to the introduction of a new entity—the neurosis of abandonment. A major part of the book is devoted to highly illuminating descriptions and characterizations of the life histories of persons who always fear, and forever anticipate, and many times provoke, rejection and abandonment.

The gestures can be: touching wood, repeating certain acts a certain number of times, etc.

If one analyzes the civilized superstitious adult, one realizes that something in him "does not believe in it"; if this individual thinks about it, he does not sincerely have faith in the magical power of his object or his gesture. But one also discovers "something in him that strongly believes in these powers." These two "somethings" (or "somebodies") are two aspects of his ego. There is an evident contradiction between his naive belief and skepticism, i.e., between the structures of these two "egos." Only the concept of a dual structure can account for this discrepancy.

Translating this into psychogenetic terms, we can say that the belief emanates from the prelogic sector and that the correction of the belief comes from the logical sector. The first sector is ruled by magic thinking; the second by rational thinking.

It is clear that the lucky objects and the phobogenic objects have an opposite effect. One is benevolent; the other malevolent. But however different these two magic processes may be, they have a common basis; this basis is the fundamental belief in the malevolence of the world which daily threatens to bring terrible deceptions. Similar beliefs have similar structures.

38. COMMENTS ON THE "CASTRATION COMPLEX"

Boys are well aware of the fact that girls "don't have" sexual organs; they do not have them because these organs cannot be seen. Some boys draw favorable, some unfavorable conclusions from this fact. A normal boy sees this anatomical difference as an advantage for himself, a sign of strength and superiority, a promise of independence. The anxious boy, on the contrary, sees in this a bad sign for himself. He puts the accent not on the presence of the organ, but on its absence in girls. His awareness that the organ can be absent, can possibly be removed, is a new trauma for him. He is quick to imagine and fear some malevolent intervention: "They will take it away from me too"; "they will cut it off," etc. Inspired by anxiety, this fantasy increases anxiety. In the first stage of primary anxiety the boy feels threatened not only in his body but also his life. In these cases, we see the fear of emasculation create anxiety which is expressed in nightmares; castration anxiety becomes connected with fear of death. At this point destruction of the visible sexual organ is confused with total destruction of the body. This is the well-known theme of *pars pro toto*.

In these fantasies, it is necessary to distinguish the letter from the spirit, the meaning of the images from the interplay of affects, to determine in what state of mind, at what stage of his development, the child created the fantasies and to determine also why he attributes such an incredible sadism to parents and educators.

Psychogenetic analysis indicates that this cruelty is not characteristic of the executor of the castration. It is only a renewed expression of the primary masochism of the subject himself, that is, of his anxiety in the face of malevolent reality. Castration fear is a second edition or a particular form of the primitive fear of the attacks of the external world. In more precise terms, it consists in attributing this old and not yet mastered fear to a new and well-determined object; the fear retains all its primitive value when it becomes secondarily attached to a particular representation. The value is that of a general and fundamental attitude about reality.

In the secondary as well as in the primary form of fear, the basic mechanism is always the same: objectivation of the complement of the affect involved. This explains the assigning of cruel and sadistic intentions to the authority objects.

Hearing our patients, one could believe that they have been the objects and victims of incredible and stupid threats. A teacher is supposed to have decided to cut the patient's penis off with a big knife; another to have told him: "If you touch it, it will rot, fall off like a rotten banana," or worse "The wolf will come and eat it up." Hearing such tales most therapists remain cautious. These affirmations are rarely exact. In my experience, they seem plausible only in about one case in twenty. These horrible fears are not provoked by inhuman parents but are the logical or prelogical outcome of the primitive anxiety of their children.

These threats have the meaning of punishment. This is a secondary elaboration related to a later stage (the oedipal stage). In these cases, we often find that harmful educational methods had been employed. The parents felt it to be their duty to treat sex play with disdain or to punish it harshly. But, however rigorous an education may be, it can rarely go so far as to suggest to a child ideas or fears of emasculation. The same fantasies are found in cases where no such sex education, in fact, none at all, took place. In many families "one just never talks about these things."

From the preceding considerations it can be deduced that the secondary stage, the mechanism of objectivation, must still be at work. In critical moments, when fears are revived, the child sees the educator in an evil light. The person whose function it is to punish him becomes at this moment a malevolent being. The fear aroused by threats and scoldings takes on the proportions of anxiety, and only primary anxiety is able to inspire fantasies as cruel as the fantasies of castration.

Let us recall here that the first form of guilt feelings consists in the fear of authority.

182   *The Ego and Prelogical Regression*

39. THE AGGRESSIVE PERSONALITY

At the basis of this personality type, we find a special reaction to the blows which reality has dealt these patients. They react in this way because they abhor the passive role of a victim. One offense calls for another, attack for counterattack. Something remains in them of the old anger against the "bad table" and the reflex impulse to hit it. This reactive impulse brings up the whole problem of the "instinct of retaliation." Without going into the complexities involved, I want to mention one genetic fact: this instinct is lacking in the individuals of the first type, the fearful individuals, and this lack seems to be one of the specific features of primary masochism, where flight reaction replaces the counterattack reaction. In contrast, the aggressive type is characterized by the development of the instinct for retaliation. It is easy to see this basic aggressiveness in many of their attitudes; even where it is not obvious it can be "felt." Individuals belonging to this type are less powerless in the face of reality and the social demands than those of the first group; however, they are much more difficult to live with. Their goal is to adjust reality and their milieu to their demands rather than to adjust themselves to the demands of reality and environment.

It sometimes happens that the natural aggressiveness of these individuals becomes excessive under certain conditions. These conditions are created by malevolent offenses of the external world, when the individual has to measure himself against a more powerful person endowed with considerable strength. The inequality of forces and this inadmissible injustice can lead the helpless weaker individual toward sadism and inspire criminal desires in him. Fantasies and dreams of this kind are frequent.

Used as a sanction, retaliation brings on its own punishment. This is its unavoidable outcome. For instance, like the individuals of the first group during the initial phase of treatment these subjects bring us dreams of passive castration in which they are the victims of this operation. Later, they bring dreams of active castration and clearly express their own desire for castrating the omnipotent authority, the malevolent being who threatens them with mutilation. It is as if they wished to mutilate their tormentor before the latter had an opportunity to castrate them. However, as a consequence, the desire to attack the powerful person reawakens anxiety which then paralyzes the patient and throws him back into the fear of being punished and again produces dreams of passive castration. In these dreams, as has been elaborated previously, the anticipated and feared misfortune is always an accomplished one. The injustice and horror implied in the passive dreams in turn outrage the victim and paves the way for reprisal. He again has active dreams. Thus we have series of circular reactions which come to an end only when a systematic analysis has freed the patient of his primary anxiety.

The theme of the alternating active and passive castration dreams is only one particular phase of the more general phenomenon from which these persons have not been able to emancipate themselves completely, despite the stimulation by the instinct of retaliation. The stimulation does not overcome their anxiety but constantly revives it. This anxiety was born where excessive aggressiveness and excessive fear met, resulting, so to speak, from the "shock" between the two.

40. SECONDARY ANXIETY

In the aggressive personality, another mechanism then arises. The subject is not made anxious, as is the fearful type, by the aggression of the malevolent object; he becomes anxious because of his own aggressiveness. Confronted with the strength of his aggressive drives, he becomes afraid. He fears retaliation. This mechanism is the inhibition of aggression by anxiety. Such anxiety arises as the result of the subject's own aggressive drives and not from anxiety which the individual of the first group experiences because he has attributed sadistic intentions to his persecutor.

Considered in relation to primary anxiety, this is secondary anxiety. This is a problem of special interest to psychoanalysts. However, I shall confine my remarks to only one point relevant to my topic.

At the stage of secondary anxiety, the patient still uses the mechanism of objectivation of affect. However, the aggressive individual differs from the fearful one in that he projects his own affect and no longer the complement of this affect. Hence the affect is aggression with all the desires and drives inspired by it and the acts which can result if the subject is not paralyzed by anxiety. Thus, full of very aggressive intentions, the subject tends to see the object of his intentions as a very aggressive person, at times sadistic, at times malevolent, in the most lethal sense of the word.

Thus this object is a secondary malevolent being no less to be feared than the primary malevolent being because, genetically, both types are closely related. In its principle and morbid intensity, anxiety has not varied while shifting from the first to the second level. Furthermore, it is easy to see that, in the second case, the aggressive individual is brought back to a situation identical to the one in which the fearful individual is thrown by primary anxiety. Therefore he uses the same kind of defense mechanisms, although in reversed order. The projection of aggressiveness in no way diminishes primitive anxiety. Before and after projection this fear retains the same intensity.

Obviously the phobic patient offers the purest example of the fearful and fleeing individual of the first type. The neurosis of abandonment, in contrast, is more complex and ambiguous because it has features of both these structures, which I have tried to contrast in order to distinguish between them. In the neurosis of abandonment, fear and aggression are combined, supplement each other, and succeed each other, but without excluding one another completely. In specific cases one or the other structure can clearly predominate: the fearful, sulky, withdrawn and fleeing "abandoned" patient can be compared to his opposite, the demanding, revendicating, accusing, arrogant, and aggressive "abandoned" individual. The first withdraws into his shell; the latter jumps, demands, threatens and plainly brings out his grievances.

In Part III we will study the reasons for such reactions, their apparent and alleged motives, and the origin and nature of their deeper mechanisms.

PART THREE

THE NEUROSIS OF ABANDONMENT

CHAPTER SEVEN

GENERAL CONSIDERATIONS OF AFFECTIVE RELATIONSHIPS

41. INTRODUCTION

DEFINITIONS

When speaking of the neurosis of abandonment, one must carefully avoid confusion between two systems of reference. In order to justify his reactions, the patient refers at times to a real and objective abandonment, and at times to a certain situation which *in his eyes* has all the characteristics of a real abandonment. This latter conception is a purely *subjective* one and may cause confusion. The most frequent and obvious confusion is the one between an imaginary and a real abandonment, between the subjective and the objective state of being abandoned.

In the sense used here, abandonment is not a real fact which we can objectively prove but is purely a question of the patient's biased interpretation and thinking. This thinking has remarkably specific and particular patterns and characteristics which must be defined.

First there is a semantic problem which stems from the ambiguity of the concept of abandonment. In the neurosis two different concepts may be present. In rare cases where the patient has actually been abandoned, the subjective concept coincides with the objective one. In most cases, however, the two concepts are radically opposed. This opposition is the most simple and, at the same time, most characteristic feature of the neurosis of abandonment.

As soon as two contradictory concepts are present, it is important not to define them with the same words. This seems to me to justify the introduction of a particular vocabulary so that the subjective and the objective idea of abandonment can be distinguished from one another.

A. *Objective (Normal) Conception*

The term "abandonment" and its derivatives in its usual sense defines two sets of ideas and actual facts: the fact of abandoning and the fact of being abandoned, or the action of abandoning and the state of abandonment. Hence in this book the term objective abandonment will be used only to refer to the *actual fact* that a relationship between two individuals has really been broken, whereby one of the partners has been the cause and the other the victim of this break.

B. *Subjective (Abnormal) Conception*

Here the physician is obliged to invent new terms which are applied only to psychopathological phenomena. They apply to clinical facts in relation to the subjective reactions of the patients. These facts have only the meaning given to them by the patient; and we will not conjecture on the real or imaginary nature of the abandonment which the patient experiences—or thinks he experiences and often deplores more than the individual who has actually experienced objective abandonment.

SPECIAL TERMINOLOGY

Subjective or imaginary abandonment—The general term applied to the body of the patient's reactions.

Abandonee—The term referring to the individual suffering from subjective abandonment. An abandonee has usually not been objectively abandoned, although the concept does not preclude such abandonment. The subjective reactions of an abandonee are very different from those of the objectively abandoned person. Indeed, there are two ways of reacting to real abandonment: a normal and adequate way and a neurotic and inadequate way.

"Abandonism" or the Neurosis of Abandonment—These terms are applied to the body of ideas and conceptions characteristic of the abandonee, or to his entire intellectual and emotional reaction pattern. Some of our patients almost make abandonism into a doctrine, somewhat like certain people regard communism. The patient who suffers from arthritis has symptoms when the weather changes; in the same way it can be said that the abandonee will experience abandonism as soon as his "own sky becomes cloudy." As we will see, there are many thunderstorms threatening on his sky and, according to the laws of magic thinking, a storm threatening is a storm already happening. The magic law of primary anxiety is, in these cases, no less rigorous than in the cases with phobias. In general, abandonism is directly proportional to the amount of affective insecurity. True abandonment is also almost always accompanied by a state of material insecurity.

42. The Fundamental Etiological Factors

An abandonee is an individual who, without any objective reasons, feels and believes himself abandoned. He has "his own reasons" for this belief; and his insistence on exposing these reasons is due to the fact that he is unaware of their infantile nature. Childhood extends into adulthood. Abandonment lies not in facts, but to my mind in the nature and the sensitivity of the person. "Nature" here refers to a primary factor of a hereditary nature; "sensitivity" points to the secondary elements derived from previous experiences.

In children who have actually been neglected, mistreated, and rejected, abandonism can be a purely acquired phenomenon;

children who lack nothing, who despite the fact that they seem to possess everything to make them happy and serene, may show abandonism which is due more to a predisposition than to an acquisition.

THE CONGENITAL OR CONSTITUTIONAL FACTOR

The most suitable term describing this factor seems to me to be "affective avidity." The abandonee's emotional greed is in sharp contrast with the affective sobriety of "inhibited" and "repressed" patients. Certain obsessional and schizoid patients retain their affective inhibition and repression throughout their lives. With the same amount of love received, some suffer hunger, others are overfed.

This clinical rule is as valid for adults as for children; or better, our patients follow this rule as if they still were children. Their avidity has retained identical objects and aims, the same thirsts and hungers, the same affects (wishes and fears), the same beliefs and concepts.

Needs and feelings constitute the *affective component*, beliefs and concepts, the *intellectual component* of the neurotic process. They are intimately related but can be studied separately. We will start with the study of the affective phenomena. These two kinds of factors—affective and intellectual—are the fundamental elements of the psychology and the behavior of patients with the neurosis of abandonment; they are at the basis of the affective relationships which these individuals establish with authority objects.

THE DOMINANT FEAR

This very general symptom can be used as an introduction to the subject. Theoretically, in our daily life, the absence of worries, fears, or dangers is enough to warrant peace of mind and to maintain our affective balance. To us this correlation is a commonplace fact which has the character of a natural law. However, this law is unknown to the abandonee. He cannot be reassured by the thought that "for the time being there is nothing to fear." In his eyes danger is always present. The rational concept of the relativity of peace of mind for human beings threatens his balance instead of assuring it; he cannot use such concepts. What he needs are certitudes; only they are able to dissipate his fears which again and again arise in him without objective reasons. His serenity obeys special laws.

The multiple objects of his periodic fears will be described in detail, but first we must study the principal object from which all others are derived. The abandonee's greatest fear is to be denied attention, to be rejected. In any lack of solicitude he invariably sees a lack of love. Whereas normally solicitude may just be one manifestation of love, in these patients there is a complete confusion between the two.[1]

This imagined rejection always results in frustration, so that this confusion is a never-ending source of unavoidable trauma. It would seem that such an endless repetition of painful experiences should lead to a hopeless affective situation which would totally destroy an individual's belief in the possibility of reaching any security in this world. Yet, on the contrary, in these patients, despite the blows of reality, disappointments and deprivations only further increase the belief in the existence of such an ideal state; this belief in turn increases their need for certainty. The suffering subject wants to be *absolutely sure that he is loved* in order to defend himself against new traumas. Thus, he fears two things: first, doubt and uncertainty; second, that the uncertainty may change into the certainty of not being loved any more. It is clear that the security of the abandonee depends on his complete assurance of being loved.

[1] The feelings and motives which are at the basis of solicitude can be very different from love and the two often do not go together.

ACQUIRED FACTORS

Besides the constitutional factors, we find acquired elements. Personal factors combine with affective avidity and continually increase it. As always, there is interaction. This point of view is in conformity with psychogenetic analysis and its therapeutic results.

These acquired factors are the result of the individual's experiences in life and the trials it presents. These factors have two special characteristics which correspond to two anomalies of the feeling of security.

The feeling of security is both extremely fragile and extremely labile. It collapses easily and needs constant reassurance in order to ward off the ever-recurring doubts and uncertainties. To the abandonee these indispensable reassurances can come only from the outside; and only certain chosen objects can bring him the certainty necessary to satisfy his security.

We see here a circle which is always the same, forever opening or closing rhythmically, the rhythm reflecting the affective state of the ego.

The basic affective avidity is activated by the fragility and the lability of internal security. This avidity is implied in these two characteristics and presupposes an insatiability of the prevailing needs and feelings. The latter, in turn, generates dissatisfaction, and this state of want becomes particularly characteristic of the abandonee. His conflict is to demand satiation without ever achieving it. This is the source of so much of the bitterness and recriminations in the aggressive individual, of so much sadness and anxiety in the fearful subject.

The patients' beliefs will provide the key to the system of ideas and axioms which are superimposed on the basic affective conflict. This system is the way in which the subject tries to explain his conflict, the origin and elements of which are unknown to him.

43. COMMON FEATURES OF PHOBIAS AND THE NEUROSIS OF ABANDONMENT

In appearance nothing resembles a phobia or nightmare less than a neurosis of abandonment. However, there are real but hidden relations between these clinical entities, and I will try to delineate their common traits.

The first is common to all neuroses: regression to the prelogical level. What characterizes the above-mentioned syndromes is that regression selectively involves the subject's affective relationships with reality and his fellow men.

The second is the production of anxiety which, in both entities, retains the patterns and contents of primary anxiety.

The third is the intervention of magic thinking with the tendency to divide reality summarily into the two categories of benevolent and malevolent elements. In the neurosis of abandonment, this double investment focuses upon the authority object. We can speak of the "magic of love" with its benevolent and malevolent aspects.

The fourth is the tendency of these patients to hang on to absolutes and to describe subjective states in absolute terms. They have a great propensity to consider the interventions of their objects as either absolutely positive and good or absolutely negative and bad.

Anxiety itself has the same character. For many of these patients, its main characteristic is the way in which it reaches the limit of what is humanly bearable. Anxiety is felt as a paroxysm, as pain which cannot possibly increase in intensity. Its disappearance, in turn, is described as absolute well-being. The law of primary anxiety is also that of "all-or-none."

In itself, the phobogenic object represents an absolute principle of death and destruction. The "great beings" created in the nightmares are absolute objects. In the neurosis of abandonment the real living authority object is also an absolute object.

The fifth is the fact that the need for security plays the same role in the biopsychic regulation of ego life in the two syndromes. In both neuroses, insecurity leads the subject into rendering certain elements of reality responsible for his suffering; these elements then become malevolent. In the neurosis of abandonment, however, the authority object is called upon to repair the damage he has inflicted. If he is able completely to satisfy the need for security and fully restore it, he becomes benevolent. In either case, his power, positive or negative, is absolute. (This special mode of regulation has great clinical importance and Chapter VIII will be devoted to a further discussion of this topic.)

The sixth point is of a more general order. The fundamental fear, as we saw, generates an imperative need for security—a problem which is extremely difficult to resolve for all patients.

For the phobic patient as well as for the abandonee, the problem is one of finding an equilibrium between the constant and often painful preoccupation with threatening misfortune and the permanent wish for its abolition. The problem is how to re-establish and assure this balance which is constantly being upset by thoughts of impending disaster.

Certain patients will use the following technique:

"During the whole night, instead of sleeping, I think about the death of my husband and children (or of parents, still alive and healthy). To imagine their death in advance is both an obsession and a relief. If I anticipate the death of the people I love most, it is only to prepare myself for it. Therefore I imagine it in the smallest details because I know that were it to happen unexpectedly, I could not live. This is why I force myself to anticipate it, to live it in advance. This seems to calm me . . ."

This is a very superstitious way of protecting oneself from the most horrible blows of fate. An anticipated misfortune will not be a misfortune once it occurs. At least, the blow will no longer be fatal. It is an insurance premium paid for life and health. But the price is high: insomnia.

Summary. The regressive mechanism of phobias and the neurosis of abandonment are intimately related. In their form and organization they differ in the features which I have just mentioned, but their basic nature is identical. This identity appears in three essential characteristics which are common to both: *the intensity of the affects involved; the prevailing use of projection; regression to magic thinking.*

44. The Obsession with Abandonment

The psychology of abandonism is highly complex. However, two elements are more clearly delineated against the unclear background of the picture, and their constancy is striking. They are characteristic of the patient's ego, of his ego life.

The first element is a kind of obsession, or obsessive feeling, more or less acute or chronic, manifest or latent, but always present at some level of the ego or in some aspect of the mind.

The second element consists in a body of more or less conscious, in fact rarely completely conscious, beliefs.

The obsessive feeling is the haunting dread of being abandoned. Therefore, these patients use a strange technique which I have called the technique of "hanging on or letting go." This is constantly used to ward off the worst blow which their object can strike against them. This blow is abandonment, as it always is the principal fear of abandonees, a fear, so to speak, inherent in their affective constitution.

As the child objectivates his fear of the fire, so the abandonee tends to objectivate his fear of abandonment by projecting its complement upon his object; to the latter he imputes mental reservations, suspicions, feelings of antipathy, bad intentions, hostile and aggressive aims. The secret goal of the object can evidently be only to abandon the subject who sees his fears as realities.

It is easy to understand that the patient's constant fear of being rejected puts the object into a difficult and tiresome situation, so much so that in the end a true break does occur. This break is the disaster feared by the more anxious or phobic abandonees. It is characteristic for abandonism to favor, even to provoke, the most painful abandonments. The patient's constant fear is manifested in various obvious ways. One of the most frequent is the fear of displeasing. The subject is constantly afraid to annoy or repulse the person whose affection he values most, whose love has the greatest power and efficacy. "All the time I am afraid that he will not be pleased with me" is a formula we hear frequently.

However, as we saw, unpleasant incidents can make other abandonees extremely aggressive. They go from recrimination to accusation, become biting and bitter. But if they become too hostile toward the omnipotent object, their fear of losing him through their own fault mounts. The prospect of deserved rejection which they expect is enough to induce them to repress their aggressiveness. This repression produces sulkiness and the "masochism of abandonment" which we will consider later (Section 74).

These patients pass with more ease and less awareness than the normal person from hope to fear, from fear to suspicion. During analysis we see alternating series; at times fear dominates, at times aggression rules.

During the phases when the aggressive abandonee projects his aggression, he transforms his object into an "affective persecutor" and tends to consider himself as the victim. He then belongs to the "persecuted-over-sensitive type." Conversely, during the phases when he expresses his grievances and shows his hostility directly, he fits in with the "over-sensitive-persecutor" type.

Due to these sudden changes, his environment considers him to be inconsistent, unstable, or bizarre. While he aspires only after security, he spreads insecurity and worry about him. The people around him never know what to expect and what to do; chances are that they will be less disappointed if they always expect the unexpected.

Such waves of contradictions make these patient's relationships neither easy nor flexible. Not only are the involved affects and needs very infantile, but they also tend to be objectivated through mechanisms which are no less infantile and which becloud objective judgment. It is very hard to put oneself in the place of these subjects because they are unable to put themselves in our place. Their laws are the laws of primitive reactions. We must either submit or give in. Relationships are a succession of crises and conflicts arising each time the subject believes the tie to be broken. This break then reactivates primary anxiety and the latter revives the objectivation of fear. This goes on until hostility and jealousy begin to interfere. They in turn lead the subject toward the projection of these affects. The aggressiveness that he attributes to his object reactivates his fear, and thus he again finds himself in a vicious circle.

The object thus is led into playing two contradictory roles: one of giving security and one of destroying security. His job is to reassure, but if he does not reassure he inspires worry and anxiety. There is no middle road.

If the object himself happens to be an abandonee, the excess of abandonism which is found in such couples greatly complicates the situation. The relationship is exposed to constant or ever-recurring dangers. It is true that abandonees seek each other out because they understand each other. Unions between them are frequent but unwise. If both partners reach a state of insecurity and mounting anxiety at the same time, each demands from the other that which he cannot give because he lacks it. Each one expects the other to change, and thus they live in expectancy of a miracle which only rarely occurs. Only simultaneous and thoroughgoing psychotherapy of both partners can achieve this miracle. Usually instead of miracles, quarrels occur. Parallel recriminations and reciprocal reproaches can only lead to separation. This kind of false union based on a double and true insecurity is destructive to any harmony or happiness. The discordance is too great between the high, ever-constant level of ideal love, conceived of in childhood and aspired to by both partners, and the low, capricious level of the concrete manifestations of two abandonees who fight each other as soon as their double insecurity sets one against the other.

Summary. The two modes of projection described in the introduction are habitual with the abandonee. The fearful type resorts to projection of the complement of the affect (aggressiveness) and the aggressive type uses projection of the affect itself. In both cases, the result is identical. The object is accused of incomprehension or injustice, later of malevolence and hostility.

In his masochistic phases, however, the subject reverses the process. Substituting contrition for aggression, he tends to accuse himself, to take upon himself the faults of his object. He considers his misfortunes as justified and deserved. Unfortunately, this pseudo-moral effort dictated by fear of abandonment only brings back insecurity and engulfs him in self-devaluation.

45. BODY OF BELIEFS

OVERVALUATION OF THE OBJECT AS A PRINCIPLE OF SELF-DEVALUATION

It is easy to deduct from the preceding considerations one of the abandonee's most firmly rooted beliefs. However, far from being apparent, this belief betrays itself at the level of the ego through indirect and veiled manifestations with several serious consequences. It is the belief in the great prestige and even supreme value of the object. I will call this phenomenon: *the functional overinvestment of the object*. I call it "functional" to show clearly that it has an important and specific function.

Clinically, three phenomena are involved whose genetic and reciprocal relations present certain variations.

1. The attachment of the subject (S) to the overvalued object (O). This is the purely affective aspect of the process. We deal here with attraction, feelings, affection, love, etc.

2. The tendency of S to overestimate O.

3. The absolute belief of S in the high value of O.

Psychoanalytically two main processes can be observed. In one, the tendency to overvalue is infantile; and in the other the absolute belief is infantile.

A. S attaches himself to O after having overinvested him. Or more precisely, he attaches himself to O because he has overvalued him.

B. S overinvests O after having become attached to him because O has become a love object.

The result is identical whether one falls in love with a person one admires or whether one admires a person because one loves him. The final situation always is an affective relationship between an inferior and anxious person and a superior being capable of reassuring him. The relationship has an unsound basis. If the object is an evolved individual who behaves as an adult while the subject remains on an infantile level, differences are bound to occur and will prevent a good and direct contact as well as a satisfactory relationship. One person looks down, the other looks up.

When this relationship is analyzed more closely, one finds that the process of overvaluation and attachment stems from very old feelings of insecurity, inferiority, and helplessness with the fear of relapsing into the painful situations which they create. Such love is based upon the need for protection. This is the reason why the subject in his anxiety integrates the problem of inferiority with the problem of love and the latter with the problem of abandonment or rather the intricate problems raised by fear of abandonment.

The tendency to fall in love with a person who protects one and allays one's fears is very human; the tendency to overvalue the protector is neurotic and typical for abandonism. Having its roots in childhood, it becomes one of the essential elements of the prelogic of relationships. It is contrary to the logic of relationships when the patient allows his health and fate to depend upon the protective function of his object. What is normal for the child is not so for the adult.

Our analyses have led us to postulate that in principle the inferiority complex precedes and dictates the choice of the object. The pre-existence of such a complex explains the tendency to overvalue the object and the belief in the reality of this overvaluation.

46. The Prejudice of the Functions

The unfortunate characteristics and consequences of these relationships need elaboration.

The subject is, or believes himself to be, happy, satisfied with himself and his fate. He has acquired his inner peace. However, his equanimity is precarious because its condition is unawareness of the self. The subject is unaware of one dangerous implication: his overvaluation of his object and his own self-devaluation, which follows inevitably. Unfortunately, ignorance of what is going on within oneself and trying to ward off a complex is not sufficient to suppress the latter. Its consequences only become more severe and longer lasting. The more one resists acquiring consciousness of what stands behind these consequences, the less one is able to escape them. In this particular case the consequences of such unawareness are numerous.

Three examples of such consequences are: (1) dissatisfaction, doubt and worry in spheres apparently remote from love (professional, social, intellectual, etc.); (2) periodic depressions; (3) absolute dependency upon the object (this theme will be elaborated later).

One striking contradiction is at the basis of these disturbances. The subject chooses his object and attaches himself to him because of his favorable influence and benevolent power. However, O possesses all the qualities necessary to keep S in a constant and unavoidable state of inferiority. O is at the same time an instrument of valuation and of devaluation. He is bound to have these two opposing actions. Comparing himself to O, S can only draw negative conclusions about himself.

Magnifying others is to minimize oneself; overrating other persons' value diminishes one's own value. The phenomenon of "macropsia," which we have discussed in dreams, bears witness to this inversely proportional relationship. "Macropsia" is characteristic of the abandonee.

This overestimation of others by the patient is due to affective reasons. Only later does the patient attempt to base it upon judgments of value. There is no reason for these judgments to be right or wrong; they are just necessary. Their function comes before their objective value. This function is to satisfy the patients' primary needs for security and protection. Many patients confuse this satisfaction with love. They do not see that their love stems from a functional overinvestment of the object and their attempts to justify their precious choice. Clear-sightedness, intelligence, and logic have little part in the choice of the object; rather it is a categoric selection which necessarily implies the superiority of the object.

Be love the son or the father of prestige, in either case love and prestige remain inextricably tied in the hearts of our patients. There is absolutely no distinction between them. The only remedy for this pathological intricacy is genetic analysis. During analysis this phenomenon always becomes apparent in dreams. As soon as the object appears in dreams, he is invested with majesty and an omnipotence which can be benevolent or malevolent. This dualism reveals the object's double function for the patient. Let us recall the dreams of Ariane, the nightmares of other abandonees and the dream of abandonment of Piaget's student. They all illustrated the relation between overvaluation of the chosen object, and affective fixation.

Maintaining these infantile concepts and beliefs has still another consequence: the prejudice of the functions.[2]

Our patients are very accessible to the world of functions and rather impermeable to the world of values. By this I mean the

---

[2] Translator's note. The terms "function" and "value" are used here by the author in the sense he has given them in his book, *Les deux sources conscientes et inconscientes de la vie morale.* There he defined them as follows: "A function is a consciously or unconsciously motivated way of satisfying needs, drives and tendencies (in the broader sense of these words), without regard for social, moral or spiritual consequences, be they good or bad. . . One may speak of 'value' only when the ego begins to transcend beyond the limited sphere of functions, that is, beyond biological, instinctual and affective needs as well as personal interests in the realm of social life" (pp. 55-56).

realistic affective values as they should preside over the choice of object.[3]

This is necessarily so because knowledge and appreciation of these values are obstacles to functional overinvestment. As we saw, the latter is based upon vital needs and infantile beliefs and not on logical concepts affording an affective orientation toward healthier goals.

Thus numerous patients become attached to persons inferior to themselves. On such points, they are not very exacting; and the less exacting, the more they are sensitive to negative functions.

Summary. The chosen object exerts a double action on the subject. The effects of this action are parallel but contradictory, and this contradiction has not always been well understood. If the object does at times have a negative and dysthymic function, he will at other times largely make up for it through his positive and euthymic function. The security-producing and valorizing influence overcompensates for the negative influence. This explains the creation of the affective relationship and warrants its duration. But as soon as the negative function predominates, the bond is destroyed; the subject must find a new object. Even when the object fulfills a negative function, the abandonee may not be aware of this devaluating action because he is too aware of or too happy about the security-producing action of his object. The inestimable value of the latter renders him blind to the former. He valuates himself highly only so long as he is tied to his object and so long as this superior person is interested in him. He clings to this belief and experiences this feeling as immediate and thus irrefutable data of consciousness. In all these subjective phenomena, we find a hidden logic which is but the affective prelogic characteristic of abandonism.

[3] See the paragraphs on the "first values" and on reciprocity and objectivity in *Les deux sources conscientes et inconscientes de la vie morale*, 2nd ed., p. 250.

47. SECURITY IN DEPENDENCY

It is characteristic for the abandonee to try to establish a very special kind of affective relationship. In a first brief review, I have only indicated its superficial structure and the elements related to ego life as the patients mention them. A more detailed account of certain particular modes of this relationship follows.

When the subject attempts to establish this kind of relationship, he has a certain goal which he attempts to attain in two successive steps. The first step is the establishment of his own security; the second, the establishment of his self-esteem. Seeking security in love, he finally discovers his own value through it. Then in the end all conditions are fulfilled to allow him to love another person.

His love thus has a functional origin. However, while developing and lasting, this love can acquire value, especially if it is shared by the object. This value then depends upon the objective, true value of the object. Love in itself has no value as long as it exists only in function of a subjective value attributed to another person. The correct application of the function, however, does not necessarily imply that the affective relationship has a value in itself; neither does it exclude it. The process, on the whole, has advantages and disadvantages. I have just mentioned the advantages and wish now to point to its greatest disadvantage.

Through his overvaluation of the object, the subject finally lives only on borrowed values. In other words, his own value is closely related to his object's value and the prestige and glory ascribed to him overshadow his real value. Dazzled by his object, the subject becomes blind to his own deficiencies; if he is conscious of his own inferiority feelings, he hardly worries about them. We find inadequate women, for example, remaining quite satisfied with themselves and happy with their lot because they are, or believe themselves to be, loved by a man of superior value.

The search for security and superiority outside oneself, born from the impulse to free oneself from an internal evil, finally leads to the most painful enslavement. The abandonee becomes entirely dependent upon his object, a dangerous and degrading position. In order not to suffer from this, his only resource is to confuse this dependency with the blind happiness it procures.

Thus, the unlimited confidence in the authority object veils and suppresses the subject's total lack of self-confidence. The newly recovered security and self-esteem conceal from consciousness the feelings of inferiority and inadequacy. However, neither their existence nor their influence are annulled.

Inversely, the loss of faith in the authority object brings with it loss of self-confidence. At the basis of the grief and pain due to the loss of the irreplaceable object or the supposed withdrawal of his total love, analysis finds intense feelings of insecurity and self-devaluation with their sorrow and despair. Desperation about the object soon becomes desperation about oneself.

48. The Object Defined by His Function

Lack of self-confidence is characteristic of the abandonee. This deficiency is the result of the fragility and lability of his feelings of security and valorization. It is the most painful symptom of the dysfunctional ego syndrome. Because of its catathymic character this symptom very often determines the choice of an object, indispensable for the affective balance of the ego.

From this point of view, the object can be defined by two propositions:

A. *The object is the person who communicates to the abandonee the most stable and strong feelings of security and is most able to preserve them;* i.e., most able to free the subject from insecurity and lack of self-confidence.

This proposition implies a second one:

B. *The object is the person who is most successful in giving the subject self-esteem,* or inversely, of freeing him from his painful feelings of inadequacy and inferiority, in a word, of *nonvalue.*

A first principle of an affective nature can be deduced from these statements. The person who will be able to carry out all four of these functions will necessarily be the most loved.

The second principle is of a more prelogical nature. The overvaluation of the loved one owes its excessive strength and reality, as well as its resistance to experience and verification, to the fact that it is rooted in a very primitive and magic belief; the belief that any human being capable of protecting another human being from suffering and trial, of dispelling malevolent powers, of inspiring security and creating value must be endowed with supreme powers. He, indeed, has all the characteristics of a magician.

CHAPTER EIGHT

THE REGULATION OF AFFECTIVITY AND THOUGHT
ITS MECHANISMS AND ANOMALIES

INTRODUCTION

In the preceding chapter I have attempted to compare the neurosis of abandonment with other illnesses which mobilize primary anxiety. I have pointed out five common points in those two clinical groups. The fifth, we will remember, consists in a special mode of regulation of affective life, needs and feelings in the deeper layers of the ego. The need for security is intimately related to the need for love; love forms the central mechanism of the regulating process.

Originally, the needs for security and love have an instinctual quality. Later, with development, these needs gain access to the ego. In the intermediary zone between the unconscious and clear consciousness, they are subjected to a first elaboration which transforms the need into a *tendency*. We then say that the fundamental tendency of the abandonee is to seek satisfaction for these two combined needs.

Still later, through its strength and the continuous pressure it exerts, this tendency becomes a drive and is finally manifested in the conscious ego as a permanent demand.

In the regulation of the ego's affectivity, two different but related kinds of factors can be found.

1. *The Affect.* The affect is the energy which activates and moves the organism. Many conditions are able to transform affect into anxiety with all its concomitant manifestations. However, the affective dynamics are not everything. The organism neces-

sarily needs an object toward which it can direct its energy and action. Affectivity in a mind devoid of images, thoughts, ideas, or concepts would operate in a vacuum. Every need, tendency, and affective demand must have a content, an object, and a definite goal.

2. *The Concept.* I have already shown that the basic concepts used by the abandonee are, on the one hand, of a prelogical nature like the one used by the patient with phobias, and on the other hand, are related to and inspired by magic thinking.

The second kind of regulating factors thus consists of a rather coherent body of magic preconcepts and prelogical axioms. These two categories while playing separate roles are complementary.

Our task will be to study these two types of factors and to analyze the role of affects and concepts in this regulatory system.

A. *THE AFFECTIVE ASPECT*

49. The Role of Affect in the Process of Regulation

The regulating process has two aspects. Considering its purely dynamic and affective aspect, one is at once struck by one phenomenon. This is the reciprocal influence of fear on the predominating need for security and vice versa.

It is self-evident that the constant fear of abandonment can only exaggerate the need for security and in turn increase the demands for additional guarantees. This functional correlation needs no further elaboration. But the subject seldom receives these guarantees in the way he would like them. Thus his security decreases more and more.

In turn, the decrease in security only increases the fear of abandonment and many patients remain caught in this vicious circle. Others, through appropriate techniques, are able to escape it. Here are two examples.

In analyzing the sexual life of one patient, I found that there had always been at least two women in his life. The number is raised to three, four, or five when he is superstitiously afraid of "breaking the tie." Even if this brings about some painful complications, the more important goal of guarantee against abandonment must be reached at any cost. In case of quarrels or a break with one of his objects there is always another one available to repair the disaster. "If one woman drops me, I always have a second one in reserve."

Another young man is attracted only to unhappy women. He has the gift of reviving, strengthening, and comforting them. While "saving" a woman, he ties her all the more closely to himself. The chance is good that she will fall in love with her helper. And the more she is tied to him, the more he becomes attached to her. This situation creates a very strong tie. Its existence and duration are independent of the amorous whims of ordinary women. It is excellent because it re-establishes the self-esteem of a man full of inferiority feelings in relations with normal women. Value and function coincide. Such an affective relationship provides exceptionally good conditions for security. While this man renders his girl friends so dependent upon him, he dominates them and thus believes himself to have avoided the danger of becoming dependent on them. He has the situation well in hand and has, so to speak, killed two birds with one stone.

50. The Process of Polarization

I often use a geometric image in an attempt to have my patients understand the activity of their predominating needs and drives. This image facilitates the explanation of the role these affects play in the regulation of ego functions and consequently of behavior.

Let us imagine that an elongated sphere occupies the central part of consciousness. This sphere has two opposite poles which we will call the pole of insecurity and the pole of security. Between these two poles, power lines with alternating repelling and attracting forces exist. The abandonee's consciousness oscillates endlessly between these two poles following these power lines. Energy is automatically mobilized along these opposing directions. Affective life becomes organized and concentrated around a central axis connecting these two poles. A perpetual movement goes back and forth and explains all the oscillations in the emotional life of these subjects: incessant oscillations of ebb and flow, ascensions and falls, euphoria and anxiety.

The striking phenomenon is the hypersensitivity of these two poles. This is due to the intricate relationships between present and past factors leading to sensitivity.

The more decisive among these factors are, no doubt, the traumas experienced in the past; and among the number of typical anxiety-producing situations, the infantile traumas are the most powerful factors producing sensitization.

Analysis regularly uncovers two contradictory series of deeply buried memories. Together they constitute what I have called "Freud's constant" and explain its lasting effect. This effect, as we remember, is made up of a more superficial fringe of conscious memories encompassing a nucleus of so-called unconscious memories. These memories can be separated into two groups; the good and the bad. Unfortunately, the good cannot erase the bad. Very often the negative affective charge of the anxiety-producing memories weighs heavier than the positive and exhilarating charge of the euphorizing memories. This predominance of the negative charge is the whole secret of the neurosis of abandonment.

This concept of parallel memory traces of two series of opposite experiences relates to the idea of two affective poles; and from a functional viewpoint they can be confused with one another.

The anxiety-producing experiences in the stormy life of these patients center around the element of insecurity; the euphorizing experiences create and are centered around the element of security.

The clinical rule of "oscillation" depends on a more general law—the law of "of mnesic (memory) or temporal participation." The present partakes of the past, just as neurotic psychology partakes of infantile psychology. This is why the present affective experience borrows from the older experiences its dynamism and characteristic modes and reproduces them.

This clinical rule is more invariable and more evident in the neurosis of abandonment than in any other neurosis, although it remains only one particular example of the more general law of affective and infantile regression.

51. The Triggering Effect

Another effect operates here related to the rule of participation between present and past. This is the triggering effect. A present incident recalls a similar incident, more or less recent, and the latter an even more remote incident. This summation can transform these incidents into a global misfortune. Each incident is confused with another past misfortune which finally is related to the original trauma whose dynamism and characteristic mechanisms then come into play. Regression depends upon these confusions. More exactly, going from confusion to confusion, the regressive process plunges to the deep level of primary anxiety. It reawakens primary anxiety and at the same time sets magic thinking into motion.

We can formulate a new principle: all excitations of the same origin and same nature have a common "affective coefficient." This coefficient has repercussions on the ego, determining the state and course of the ego's affects. A very old and very strong impression can thus be relived, remaining intangible and not reaching clear consciousness. What is remarkable here is the permanence of this coefficient explaining the permanence of the feeling of certain and imminent danger.

In the abandonee the traumatic character of the repeated oscillations is the result of these cascading series of confusions in psyche and time. The oscillations are the incessant changes from security to insecurity.

There is only one remedy for this traumatic action, and the patient uses it instinctively as if he were a child: benevolent magic thinking.

An objectively innocuous insecurity situation becomes subjectively severe when it mobilizes emotions related to former traumas and reproduces the ideo-affective elements contemporary to the trauma. This is why, when the patient lives with his object, apparently minimal incidents can assume a tremendous importance due to their powerful subjective resonance. To the laymen the disproportion between fact and reaction is apparent and offensive; they are unable to see the reason for it because they ignore the following general law: facts of this order are independent of the rational and normal laws of natural psychic causality. They are ruled by the laws of a kind of precausality which governs regressed affectivity and regulates the association of actual affective phenomena with older traumas. This is the "law of summation" based on a complete lack of rationality and logic.

This is why an indifferent incident can become an emotional trauma, a true and severe trauma characterized by a brusque shift from the positive pole of security to the negative pole of insecurity.

52. Incidents Becoming Misfortunes

The intensity of this internal resonance is proportionate to the amount of oscillations between security and insecurity. Because of these oscillations, an insignificant incident becomes an accident, the accident a disaster. It is the abandonee's nature to pass from the expectation of his misfortune to its accomplishment and from the accomplishment to a renewed expectation of disaster.

These incidents may originate from either the subject or the object. I will restrict myself to the presentation of a few examples of those originating from the object. Their common feature is the discrepancy between their objective and subjective importance. This discrepancy is due to the fact that the subject relates everything to himself; his egocentricity makes him interpret the incident and then react according to his interpretation. The motives for certain of the object's thoughts, gestures, attitudes and behavior can be completely unrelated to the subject or the affective relationship between subject and object. Nonetheless, the subject immediately discards the objective motives. Even if later the object reveals these objective motives, he will rarely be able to convince the subject, who will retain all his suspiciousness.

The following incidents belong in this category:

The object shows distraction, lack of attention or reticence; criticism or a justified reproach; an absent-minded, sad, or severe look; a slightly brusque gesture; a rough and perhaps explosive tone of voice; mockery; "a passing cloud"; and especially silence which is almost always interpreted as ominous; pleasant things which happen at the wrong moment; teasing, a trick or a joke.

A second type of incident hurts even more: not to be there at the right time. Justified absence; temporary and inevitable separation; necessary departures; the sole fact of taking care of someone else, or worse, of prefering him.

When something which "is not worth it" produces a severe trauma, one must think of externalism. The disproportion of the reactions is the sign of an intense externalism rendered increasingly severe by the duration and the evolution of the neurosis. The abandonee sees only the images and symbols of love, only the signs of feelings. Their deeper sources of value escape him.

This important theme of the little incidents which become big accidents will be further developed in Section 58. On the other hand, we have the great realistic and irreparable accidents, the catastrophic triad of separation, loss of the love object, and true abandonment. They will be amply discussed later on. Their effect is to activate profound insecurity and to assure its functional predominance for a long time.

53. The Process of Exogenous Securitization

To speak of poles of security is to use an image which will help us to understand the subject's mentality. The affectivity at the disposal of his ego tends to be mobilized into two opposite directions according to negative and positive influences of present reality combined with the corresponding influences of the past. It can be said that the ego is polarized. Of course, the contents and modalities of the mobilized memories do not have to be evoked or recalled in order to exert their dynamic action. In general, anxiety is reproduced without evocation of the past, or at least is independent of it. In his consciousness the subject relates anxiety immediately and entirely to the present incident.

The two phases of the accident

We shall call "accidents" all events leading to loss of security or of self-esteem. The characteristic feature of this phenomenon in abandonism is that its cause is external. The determining factor is not internal to the subject but external to him. It is in the object or emanates from him. It is related to thoughts, feelings, and the behavior of the person from whom the subject derives his value and to whom he owes his security. To be loved by the object seems an infallible token of security and happiness, and inversely the withdrawal of his love brings *a*-security and anxiety. The fear of losing the object is enough to produce a loss of the feeling of security.

This process is called *exogenous securitization*. Unable to find any security in himself, the abandonee is obliged to look for it on the outside. In this way, his situation is that of the small child. Security, when it cannot be derived through an endogenic process, has to be communicated from outside the self. This communication of security is the role of the authority object, as it previously was of the mother. During childhood exogenous securitization is a normal process, indispensable and vital. It is in conformity with the laws of primary realism. In the adult, on the contrary, it constitutes a severe abnormality and is proof of the persistence of the realism underlying neurotic externalism.

54. Sex and the Security Function in the Love Relationship

The following analysis will have as its theme a particular and relatively simple type of affective relationship between two individuals: the authority object (O) and the subject (S) who is an abandonee.

One feature clearly distinguishes this couple from a so-called normal couple. In the latter, the two members are at the same time object and subject. And if it is a love relationship, of course, sex prevails over the security function.

These two principles, which can be considered as a general law, are lacking in the relationship, O-S. In the latter, the security function prevails over sexual activity. This inversion of a general law sheds some light upon an apparently puzzling clinical fact. In the life histories of abandonees, relationships of a more or less sublimated homosexuality or relationships tinged with homosexuality are not rare and can be found to alternate with apparently normal heterosexual relationships. I say apparently because phases of impotence and frigidity in the heterosexual relations are frequent. However, this is not our problem.

Our problem lies in the series of clinging relationships about which women patients say: "I don't trust men any more . . . therefore I turn back to women" (e.g., toward the mother); and the reverse is true of men.

Finally a third feature characterizes the couple, O-S: the triumphant "subjectivism" of the subject. I have already alluded frequently to this trait and will again in the future. However, one must not attribute too great a significance to this subjectivism and draw hasty conclusions. Even in apparently normal love relationships absolute objectivity cannot be postulated. Love and objectivity are different and the former does not favor the latter. The most healthy individual under the sway of sexual love can hardly be entirely objective toward his object. The phenomenon of overestimation of the sexual object is very well known. We can admit that in friendship objectivity is possible, but in love it is doubtful.

Furthermore, the relationship, O-S, can be founded on friendship, affection, and tenderness as well as on sexual love. Its principles and goals are more often the differentiated modes of affectivity rather than simple sexuality.

55. THE ROLE OF THE OBJECT

In order to assume and fulfill the function of an entirely satisfying authority object, the latter must possess varied and rare gifts, pertaining to affectivity rather than to pure intellect. First, and most important to the subject who is always ready to worry even without objective reasons, is the ability to reassure him. O has to give the subject self-confidence and convince him of his usefulness and value; he has to assure him that he is worthy of esteem and love. Moreover, the subject has to feel esteemed and loved such as he is, for what he has, in spite of his shortcomings.

It is important for O to appreciate S's qualities rather than to blame his shortcomings, to express praise rather than criticism. S often worries that his shortcomings may antagonize not only his protector but also other people about him. He is well able to make up for his faults by gratefully and tenderly demonstrating his affection and by protestations of love and admiration, the sincerity and charm of which are made possible by his happiness.

Finally, one absolute assurance is indispensable to his contentment. He must have a special place, play a unique role, in the feelings and thoughts of his object; he must be the one who counts more than any other person. He must be "the chosen one," in title and fact. Only this tight little bundle of certainties can preserve him from jealousy.

Thus we see that the conditions and motives of the abandonee's jealousy are usually more imaginary than real. The problem raised by this kind of jealousy, which is half-way between naiveté and maliciousness will be investigated further in the following chapters.

These are the essential conditions (among other less constant ones) which a so-called "relation of security" has to fulfill in order to attain its goal. Through simple deduction, we can see the second function of such a relation: the valorization of the subject.

S "has a value" because he counts or believes himself to count absolutely for a person to whom he attributes such a very high value. He measures and proves his own value by the esteem shown to him by O. The best proof O can give him is always to love him *just as he is.*

Of course, the subject has other interests and needs in life, but he can devote himself to them only if his mind is at peace. His aptitudes for and inclinations toward satisfying his personal tastes or accomplishing his professional or home duties depend on his general mood, his *Stimmung.* If he feels sufficiently sure of his own worth, his mood is good and favorable for work. If he does not, the reverse occurs.

Thus a high conjuncture governs his personal life, thought, and social action. The latter develop proportionally to the quality and efficacy of the relation of security and self-value. In the last analysis, every affective relationship has but this one aim of security and valorization. The value borrowed from the object is more highly prized than the subject's own personal value. Of the latter, he is only dimly aware, whereas the former imposes itself on consciousness as an immediate certainty. This certainty sustains him, encourages him, makes him act. When he is forced to rely only on his own value, about which he has so many doubts, he is helpless. Doubt prevents him from realizing his own value into concrete and valuable performances.

This is how he proceeds in order to shield his feeling of self-value from the blows which could arise from his inadequacy and inferiority complexes. Exogenous securitization and exogenous valorization usually go together.

56. The Regulation of Suffering

A frequent source of suffering is disagreement with the object. Any disagreement is extremely painful to the abandonee. He hates it, it may even be a phobia with him.

In a normal relationship, certain things are all right, others are not. If there is disagreement on one point, this does not mean that agreement cannot be reached on other matters. The normal individual does not confuse the part with the whole. To the abandonee disagreement has an ominous meaning because it forbodes a break. The suffering which arises results from the triggering of insecurity. It reaches its highest degree when the break takes place. But from what does the abandonee really suffer when he feels abandoned?

He suffers not so much from the fact per se, from the actual loss of his object, but rather from its subjective consequences. He suffers not from the grief which the normal person experiences in such circumstances but more from a loss of subjective security and self-value. Actually, on the level of function, objects are interchangeable.

The suffering emanates directly from this double loss of security and self-value. Through its power and spontaneity, this loss veils and later extinguishes the pain due to the loss of love. The fact that a precious joy—the joy which one experiences when expressing one's love to a loved one—that this is from now on unavailable, plays only a secondary role. The importance of the love object ceases with his or her functional role. The loss per se of the object is confused with the loss of his functions.

There is no doubt that the origin of this almost reflex-like way of reacting and suffering has its roots in infantile egocentricity and is ruled by its laws, analyzed and described by Piaget.

57. A Form of Depression Intrinsic to the Ego

There is a state of suffering indicating a block in the system of affective regulation of the ego. It is manifested by an intense depression, which itself is the expression of a lowering of "ego tonus." This is an extreme reaction which can follow the loss of the object, but usually is only one particular phase in a general process.

I do not use the term depression in the sense of a lowering of tension, or a state of "psychasthenia," such as Janet described it, i.e., a lowering of energy affecting the whole psychological activity or selectively one or the other faculties of the mind (intellect, will power, action, higher social behavior, etc.).

I would define this depression precisely in the following terms: a dysfunctional process of the ego accompanied by a particular affective state which is characterized by affective suffering (in popular language, demoralization) with sadness, despondency, and dull anxiety (usually interrupted by acute attacks).[1] We know that depression can be psychogenic, determined by adverse external circumstances and by the infantile superego and unconscious (masochistic) tendencies; or it can be related to organic factors as in the endogenous melancholia.

There is, however, a third cause which has been given relatively little attention. This factor is the feeling of inadequacy which through an implacable gradation can end in an acute feeling of devaluation. Fixed ideas are related to this feeling. Ideas of total failure, "end of everything," irreparability, etc. Patients express these ideas readily: "Everything is lost, is over for me; I am good for nothing. Why go on? I will never come out of it; I am less than nothing; just good enough to regret my messed-up life." In this state, the depressed person sees every-

---

[1] In more familiar terms, the "blues," a "black mood," "to be down in the dumps," etc.

thing as "black." The "blackness" of the past colors the future. It amplifies failures and disappointments. Having lost faith in himself, the depressed person has no faith in anybody. He has no interests. His powers of resistance wear out. This can reach the point of intense aversion for action, people and life. His final state is not that of the well-known despair but the less known feeling of nonvalue. At this zero point there is nothing more to lose. Having reached rock bottom, one is no longer in danger of sinking any lower. Even though this is a state of depression, it brings great relief.

How does the patient attempt to explain his depression? Spontaneously, he relates it to his failures, disappointments, griefs, deceptions, and finally to his loneliness, thus mistaking the effect for the cause. As he has lived it, this causal relationship is correct. However, it is only secondary. What should be called the primary, direct and real causes escape him. Being unconscious of the real determining factors, he substitutes for them those that trigger his reaction.

The true and primary factors consist not in the results of the process of devaluation (feelings of inferiority and helplessness) but in the process itself. In the abandonee this prelogical system is both most powerful and most unconscious. Hence the real etiology of his depression escapes him. Here we have a very important preconscious causal link which we have to explain to the patient before starting a deep psychoanalysis.

The process of devaluation, as I have pointed out, is done by the ego. It is made up of a number of reactions which are characteristic of the ego and which, so to speak, are in the "ego's nature." On this point, one problem needs to be clarified. A depression necessarily affects consciousness. It is defined by a state of consciousness with all the negativism which goes into it. An "unconscious depression" would be a contradictory term.

In short, a depressive state is always an ego state. However, this does not prevent it from being determined by extrinsic causes or motives, that is, by causes foreign to the ego and independent of it.

But besides the extrinsic forms of depression there exists an intrinsic form, the causes and motives of which are in the ego, originate in the ego and influence consciousness directly. I can think of no better term for this intrinsic form than *depression of ego origin*. This is the counterpart of the "superego depression," an already well-accepted designation, meaning a depression which has its origin in the infantile superego.

The intrinsic form due to devaluation generally plays an important role in psychopathology. In neuroses of insecurity, inferiority, and abandonment in particular, this role becomes most important. I have the impression that it is often confused with the extrinsic forms and that this confusion produces errors in therapy. A study remains to be made of the pathogenic relations between these two categories of depressions. It is of the highest interest but beyond my subject.

On the basis of these considerations we can draw a general conclusion. *If anxiety is the result and evidence of the loss of all security (which is well known) it is also, and especially, the result of the loss of all self-esteem (which is less well known.)*

58. Remarks on Affective Realism and Its Forms in the Abandonee

Again the question of terminology must be raised. In speaking of adults it is correct to speak of affective externalism. The frequency of this process is such that anyone can find examples. It is the most outstanding symptom of the neurosis of abandonment.

However, we must consider externalism as an exogenous determination of affective states of the ego. This causal mode is always related to certain reasonings which are typical of the abandonees. Paul, the seven-year-old child discussed in Section 77, can serve as an example. Very jealous of his younger brother and sister, Paul suddenly becomes ill. The family physician prescribes a rest in a high altitude. Here is the reasoning of the little abandonee: "If mother has sent me away to this unpleasant and cold place, it is because she wanted to get rid of me; she does not like me any more and prefers Peter and the little one."

This is a way of feeling rather than a way of reasoning. It is a mixed process which I will call the *prelogical axiom*. It emphasizes the relationship between prelogic and primary realism in adult neurotic thinking.

The following are illustrations of the type of reasoning presented by abandonees, all of which were voiced as complaints:

"He is absent-minded; thinks of something else, not of me."

"He has no consideration for me, at least not the kind I expect."

"She has not telephoned."

"She knew I would be here this evening . . . and she did not come."

"He has forgotten my birthday."

"He seemed so happy when he left me, and so displeased when he came back."

THUS:[2]

"He thinks of someone else."

"He does not love me any more."

"She seems detached."

"I don't count any more."

"He is angry at me."

"He is dropping me."

[2] See Section 59.

Clearly the needs and demands, desires and fears of S are expected to magically dictate O's thoughts, words and acts. O has to partake in the affective life of S; this intimate participation arising intuitively between the two is the fundamental cause for their relationship. If S has a desire, O has to have it too. He must love or dislike the same things and the same people. Difference is confused with disagreement and the latter with disunion. Everything that threatens this participation produces a sudden decrease in S's feelings of value and security. This is why O's behavior is interpreted as an abandonment about to happen or one that has already happened. Every complaint is both an appeal and a reproach.

There are three basic principles for these types of egocentric interpretations.

1. S builds up his system of impending abandonment before inquiring. He jumps to his conclusions at once instead of investigating what personal motives O may have. He becomes upset before inquiring about objective reasons behind O's doing or not doing something, behind his adopting one viewpoint instead of another. The usefulness and benefits of objective inquiry remain ununderstood or unadmitted; or they are completely neglected in the name of the principle of the "same opinion." This principle states that an object worthy of the name must never disagree with the subject. If O defends his viewpoint, he is wrong. If he sticks to it, he rejects, despises, or offends S. This principle can assume an amazing strength when the concepts are determined by infantile affects or, at least, conditioned by them.

2. Without being aware of it, S establishes a second principle. He behaves as if he considered his feelings as existing only for themselves; as if his needs, fears and wishes had an absolute value. The mere fact of their existence is enough to justify their

characteristics and demands. S cannot see or conceive of O applying the same principle. If he applied it, O would ruin the principle and S's whole system would crumble. Being considered as "absolute data," a need, wish or feeling cannot be relative to the need, wish or feeling of another individual. All reversibility of viewpoints is thus excluded.

3. For evident reasons, all reciprocity is excluded too because as soon as his affectivity enters into action S cannot put himself into O's place.

We can see how a tyrannical need for security, and for self-value seeking satisfaction and guarantee at the expense of the object's autonomy and without respect for his person, can bring the subject back to complete externalism.

Such a concept of relationships would be three times "realistic" (in Piaget's sense of the word) because neither objectivity, relativity, nor reciprocity have any place in it. In our patients, three modes of externalism frequently occur. Even though intellectual in appearance, this externalism is the result of affectivity, an affectivity whose externalism proves its infantilism. At its source are needs and wishes, emotions and feelings. There is no exception to this rule. Reality (in this case the objects or, more generally, the non-self) has to conform to the various feelings of the ego. All autonomous attitudes or reactions on the part of the object are conceived of or felt by the subject as a rupture of their pact. Independence is synonymous with unfaithfulness. Spontaneity of the object is seen as callousness, originality as lack of tact. All these concepts are confused.

Where no affective realism exists, the relationship between two individuals attached to each other and largely dependent upon one another gains in flexibility and reciprocal tolerance. Each one feels free to have projects, plans, his "own little program." He has no fear about realizing them because he knows that the other does the same. Neither one will feel devaluated because the other acts independently. The question of devaluation thus is solved. Whenever two evolved people live together, it is often necessary that their programs be integrated reciprocally. When this integration is required it takes place easily. And we then can see that reciprocity in an autonomous relationship is the highest force for self-valuation when it is based upon the rigorous principle of objective inquiry, honestly carried out by both sides. Discussions are conducted by equals, with frankness and without undue affect.

All these sound concepts and healthy realizations of life are inaccessible to the abandonee.

B. *THE CONCEPTUAL ASPECT*

59. The Abandonee's Axioms

"Therefore he does not love me any more." "Therefore she rejects me." The word "therefore" opens the important chapter of prelogic axioms. Why does the abandonee make such a systematic use of these axioms? What is their function to him? Broadly speaking, he uses them to justify his dominant emotions and to provide them with a more or less stable body of reasons. This set of reasons has the sole purpose of providing an explanation for the mechanisms of increasing security and self-esteem which take place in his ego but which he cannot accept passively as a moved or resigned spectator. This persevering search for explanations is too important for our understanding of the abandonee to allow us to neglect the conceptual aspect of the general process of regulation.

We will start with an attempt to analyze the first group of prelogic concepts directly accessible to the psychotherapist's observation. In general they are syllogisms whose devastating character will soon be apparent to the reader (at least to the reader who does not suffer from a loss of self-esteem and does not customarily use these mechanisms to rebuild it from external sources). This leads us to the second group of prelogic concepts: the *need for the absolute* and its close connection with an intense aversion for the relative.

60. THE PRELOGIC SYLLOGISMS OF "ALL-OR-NONE"

The popular expression of "all-or-none" aptly states the abandonee's fundamental principle by which he feels obligated to regulate all his spontaneous reactions. The believer in "all-or-none," reasons approximately in the following way: "It is too overwhelming; I can't help it; I want all and I would rather have nothing than not enough. I would rather have none than a half or a quarter." In some way he finds again in the nothing the absolute he has lost. This way of reasoning is obviously only a way of feeling, determined by the basic affective avidity.

CORRELATIVE AXIOM

"What I can get is not enough if somebody else [the assumed rival] can get as much as I do." "Why should I renounce personal privileges or special favors? They are only a fair reward for my absolute love for the person who grants me these favors."

In any case, if a third person, supposedly a rival, makes his appearance, at once what was formerly relative becomes absolute, that is, absolutely negative or nonexistent. Ths is a very important point. Jealousy, justified or imaginary, stems from an inability to share. Sharing is the very essence of relativity. Banning uniqueness and exclusiveness from affective relationships, sharing permeates them with relativity. For the abandonee, uniqueness means that the object is required to harbor for the subject feelings which are completely different from those he experiences toward other people, therefore unique in kind and manifestations. For the abandonee, sharing destroys the value and function of love.

EXAMPLES OF TYPICAL AXIOMS

What we have just formulated in a condensed form is derived from innumerable utterances, so similar to each other that one could almost believe that the various patients had conspired to agree upon them.

Mrs. B.: "If my husband tells me that a woman is very good-looking, charming, or intelligent, or that she speaks and writes well ... I get all upset, horribly ill at ease. Painful thoughts occur to me ... therefore, *I* am ugly, or repulsive, or stupid, or unable to express myself. Therefore he prefers her and wants to leave me."

Mr. C.: "If my girl friend mentions or insinuates that a man is handsome and seductive, it absolutely means that I am not. If she hints that he does something well, it means that I do it wrong. These compliments to somebody else deprive me of all assurance and self-confidence. Doubts arise; maybe I'm not worthy of her, and then anxiety and fears that she might love him because he deserves it more."

Miss M.L., age nineteen, declares bitterly and categorically: "When mother says that Denise [the younger sister] is pretty, friendly and nice, she means that *I* am ugly, unlovable and bad. If one girl is pretty, I am ugly. If one girl is very pretty, I am very ugly. Mother prefers Denise and she really made me feel it." This is an allusion to a long and interminable series of conflicts with mother and sister. Believing her cause lost, M.L. clung to her mother all the more and later resorted to recriminations. After the birth of more siblings, all said to be very lovable, the patient became more demanding and complaining. "If mother continues to be so attached to them, she cannot love me any more and will never again love me...all is finished between us, etc." Nothing could make her relinquish this idea, and then out of her feeling of lacking any self-value, she began to suffer from a depression originating in the ego. Anxiety attacks and school failures followed. Although not beautiful, M.L. was pleasant looking and intelligent. She had always been at the head of her class, and had come to feel that this privileged position was reserved for her. It was hers so long as her mother preferred her to her sister and in proportion to her mother's favors. When she lost the belief that she was mother's favorite, she also lost confidence in her intelligence and abilities. The inevitable accident happened soon. One day M.L. came out second in mathematics, being supplanted by another girl. This constituted a new usurpation of a well-deserved right and a new trauma. Unfortunately the teacher warmly congratulated the lucky rival, at the same time criticizing the patient "with much contempt." After this M.L.'s school work declined rapidly until she was and remained last in her class. Nothing was left of her real talent for mathematics. "When the teacher said that Sally [the rival] had been more studious, she meant that I was lazy. That is why she liked Sally better and had no more confidence in me. So why should I try?" "If I am not first any more, I am not good at anything any more. I don't count with the teacher any more...And yet I loved her so much." (As a substitute for the deficient mother.) "If Sally is first it means that teacher loves her, and her alone, and not me any more." Deprived of any affective support, M.L. lost ground and her intellectual proficiency fell to zero.

It is easy to reverse the unhealthy and negative axioms into positive and beneficent, highly self-valuing ones. The day came when M.L. was warmly complimented by her mother with an unexpected display of tenderness. This one act was sufficient to restore to its prior intensity the feeling of security which had been destroyed by the abandonment. Her parents had just been divorced and her mother, now also abandoned, turned back to M.L., her oldest daughter. This "benevolent return" was enough to readjust M.L. to her school situation and study requirements. She recovered her abilities in mathematics and soon was first in her class again.[3]

This patient, insatiable in her search for love and sick with jealousy, is characterized by an exclusive and extreme intolerance of sharing. At school as well as at home she must be either first or last. It is all-or-none.

The essential problem of the necessity to share can be reduced to a simple dilemma:

Either: he loves me and therefore he cannot love another.

Or: he loves another and cannot love me.

To love half is not to love at all. In this argument the patient confronts himself with two contradictory positions and leaves the choice to the love object. Therefore he stubbornly defends his expectations and is extremely dependent upon his loved object. All of these patients reason in this way, implicitly or unconsciously. None of them ever has formulated clearly and logically the two propositions of the abandonee's dilemma. They ignore the fact that they established this dilemma in their childhood and still live according to the conclusions they drew from it.

ABANDONISM AS A SUCCESSION OF CONFUSIONS

It is important to relate to each other these axioms and syllogisms created by an affectivity which has not yet reached the end of its evolution. The principles which they imply provide us with the axiomatic elements of abandonism.

[3] See my discussion of a similar case in "L'antinomie ou l'homonomie médico-pédagogique." *Revue Suisse d'hygiene,* 1946.

Our study is certainly far from complete. It will only reach completion when we can draw conclusions from our research about the *genesis* of the primary feelings of value and security in the child. Meanwhile, the elements already at our disposal permit a first attempt at synthesis.

In love relationships the abandonee becomes involved in a certain number of confusions:

He confuses a fair division of his loved one's feelings among several persons with an unfair sharing. And along with this he foresees a diminution, later a complete loss, of these feelings for himself. In other words, he confuses sharing with a weakening and later a loss of love, and consequently a loss of his object.

Differentiation of feelings and sharing are synonymous with abandonment.

Abandonment is synonymous with withdrawal of love, and vice versa.

Uncompromising demands are the result of these confusions, but the confusions make for a better understanding, beyond the superficial or pretended motives, of these demands and their deeper meaning. These motives then cease to appear inadmissible or extravagant. We refuse to connect these attitudes with pure jealousy or the refusal to share with pure egotism. The refusal to share has its own very strong and complicated affective prelogic which is not found in real egotism.

Summary. The abandonee loves absolutely anyone who loves him absolutely. He cannot love anyone who loves him only relatively. In the latter case his love, that is, his disappointment, is expressed by hostile, demanding or sulking behavior.

In appearance, there may seem to be an absolute reciprocity in this relationship. However, such a reciprocity is deceiving and illusory. Being so absolute is enough to condemn it. The abandonee imposes his own law upon his object and forbids him to differentiate his feelings. This is the fundamental mechanism of the abandonee's false reciprocity.

61. THE THREE CHARACTERISTICS OF A HEALTHY FEELING

The psychopathology of abandonism is so complex and varied that it defies effort at condensation. Therefore, I have limited myself to general mechanisms and principles. A special work would be necessary to outline the clinical psychology of this neurosis. It would include a systematic analysis of its various forms with their corresponding symptoms.[4]

Again I will conclude with the three principles related to the most usual consequence of the subject's "security and value relationship" with his authority object.

Since he compares everything to this relationship and to the exceptional qualities of his object, the abandonee condemns himself to impersonality in his affective and intellectual life. Beyond the superficial gilding, his own interests are dull and neutral.

If in the beginning man lacks autonomy, autonomy must later develop within his personality. The lack of an autonomous personality remains the stigma of the abandonee. This anachronism is irreversible and puts an insuperable obstacle to the acquisition of three essential qualities which every positive feeling in a healthy and fully evolved individual should possess:

A. Spontaneity.

B. Intrinsic value.

C. The power to safeguard the general feeling of internal security and to strengthen it through living in harmony with it instead of disturbing or corrupting it.

One decisive and always moving experience is forever denied

---

[4] Such a work has been published by Miss G. Guex. It is a welcome and useful complement to this present book.

to the abandonee. Its principle lies in the "valorization" of the individual's own feelings; its result is the establishment of a harmonious relationship between the value of these personal feelings and the value attributed to them by the person who is their object. The beloved person can only attribute a value to the subject's feelings and personality proportionally to the value the subject himself attributes to these feelings, and vice versa. Hence, an exclusive selection ceases to be an abnormal phenomenon because it is reciprocal. A normal selection is free and mutual. Every evolved individual feels its charm. Self-esteem and security are at the basis of a mutual and autonomous choice and not the result of it. Each partner can then give spontaneously without first expecting or asking. The roles are reversible.

62. The Need for the Absolute

Many allusions have been made to the *absolutism* inherent in the abandonee's thinking. It is certain that infantile traumas largely contribute to its development.

We have stressed the rapidity and the magnitude of the oscillations in the abandonee's emotions. He easily plunges to the depths and just as easily is transported into seventh heaven, from which he again falls even deeper. Passing from euphoria to deepest anxiety, he always goes from the absolutely positive to the absolutely negative. Paradoxically, it seems that this trying order of things is more bearable to him than the stability which stems from a sense of relativity in life and in affective relationships. This paradox can be explained. Relativity of feelings deprives a relationship of its meaning and function so far as the abandonee is concerned. Characteristically the abandonee will use the mechanisms of abandonism whenever his basic tendencies are not entirely satisfied. A partial abandonment is total to him. An approximate feeling is viewed as a negative one. He tends to see what is wrong not what is right. An affective relationship that is not very close does not deserve to be called by that name.

If the tie somewhat loosens, this means a break. Anxiety transforms this premonition into a cause for a break. It can be said that relative causes and facts come to have absolute effects. Contrary to all logic, this is the way the abandonee persistently views events. In analyzing his retrograde reasoning, we attempt to find some "logic" in his illogic, to get at the root of and define the prelogical concepts on which he bases his behavior.

The demand for an absolute tie can only be made and maintained if the three principles of relativity, objectivity and reciprocity are ignored. This demand forces the relationship to function outside reality, and every contact with reality will threaten to destroy it.

However, it is understandable that the abandonee cannot easily renounce his demands and that he remains blind to the contradictions which reality provides for his fantasies. Feeling his need for absolute security defeated and questioned at every turn, his best way of appeasing this need and satisfying it is to call for absolute values.

There are three such absolute values: duration, continuity, and the selective (preferably exclusive) character of the relationship. To the abandonee, happiness loses its reality if it has to be interrupted, weakens, or has to be shared. Sharing is damaging to love, not only in its realization, but even more in its very essence. These maxims are very close to the absolutism characteristic of the child who is fearful because of jealousy or jealous because of fear.

In contrast, when a love relationship or friendship is based on rationally and consciously applied principles, its solidity and true character are best assured. Of course, the difficulty of basing affective life on these judicious principles will always exist for everyone.

For the abandonee this difficulty is insurmountable because of the goal he stubbornly tries to achieve. His aim is not predicated on the relationship itself, does not consist in a shared love, in the charm of a life in common founded on reciprocity and autonomy. His immediate objective is to establish and consolidate a kind of total affective and intellectual participation. This will of course ruin all true reciprocity. Thus he establishes not so much a relationship as such but a mutual and reciprocal identification which ruins all true reciprocity. In order to exist and be realized, true reciprocity demands that there be two personalities and not "one in two" or "two in one." Such a symbiotic union demonstrates that the two partners are not united on the level of mature personalities. On the mature level one principle reigns: one human being attaches himself to another because he justly appreciates and honestly respects that personality in its essence and uniqueness.

63. Relationships of Normals and Abandonees

Every healthy and fair relationship has three points of support: relativity, objectivity, and reciprocity (a logical relationship of this sort will be abbreviated by the letter L).

The abandonee's logic, as opposed to this one, is quite different and is based on affective prelogic as it creates and develops abandonism (abbreviated by the letter P).

This abbreviated summary is useful for the formulation of the following principles:

RELATION L

The relativity of the bond can be absolutely satisfying and the source of full and lasting security. This implies and reveals that

a process of endogenous securitization has been solidly established in both partners. To maintain his ego in a functional
balance, neither partner needs to resort to the other and constantly lean on him. Both can dispense with the relapses into
the precarious process of exogenous securitization and valorization. Renouncing this false and regressed reciprocity, they are
in a good psychological position to apply the correct and progressive modes of reactions.

RELATION P

Inversely in our patients an absolute value ceases to have any
value when it becomes a relative value. Its diminution is confused with suppression. Its relativity implies its nonexistence. A
relaxed, weakened, intermittent, or shared tie is synonymous
with separation. This source of confusion becomes a source of
anxiety because it is a source of insecurity. The absolute value
of feelings is the best guarantee for a security which is conceived
of as total or not at all. This absolute value safeguards the
asphaleia and both concepts become one.

Correlatively, the state of insecurity leads the anxious person
to attribute an absolute value to any feelings which could end
this state. Thus the abandonee is logically inclined to attribute
a high value to his own feelings proportionally to the high value
he bestows upon his object's feelings for him. His value does not
exist per se; it is simply a ratio.

The abandonee negates the very goal for which he establishes a relationship by using the means best suited to render his
goal inaccessible. An absolute tie is a myth, even when an adult
believes himself capable of basing it upon infantile realism.

It is on the basis of the infantile magic of feelings that he tries
to establish it. This kind of total and mystical love, familiar to
all therapists, is pervaded by affective magic. Because of it, adult
abandonees develop and maintain their affective concept. How-

ever, common sense has always known that absolute feelings are beyond the possibility of human beings, and that striving for them will always disturb relationships.

64. "Affect as a Whole" and the Irresponsibility of Feelings

The abandonee, as we have said, has a tendency to look upon an affective relationship as an unsharable whole. This idea of totality covers the concept of absolute affective participation mentioned above. The two concepts are in reality one.

To some, such an ideal of totality may seem to be the highest possible of all human relationships. Actually it is due to an arrest in development. If affective evolution does not go beyond the stage of affective realism, the adult will remain fixated at this stage and be condemned to externalism.

Under these conditions, the subject has not acquired a capacity which is essential to the establishment of his autonomy and unity: the sense of his own personality. This means the capacity to assume the responsibility of his own feelings for himself and his feelings for his object. Before examining the lack of this capacity, it is important better to define the concept of "affect as a whole" because both these genetic phenomena are related.

This idea of "affect as a whole" is best seen in another type of couple, both abandonees (S1 and S2). These two individuals relate to each other quickly and establish a fusion of their emotions. These emotions form a sort of a whole which transcends the individuals who created them and who therefore become impersonal or depersonalized. Their feelings are no longer of a subjective unity, but a whole external to the individuals. Thus is formed a sort of superindividual which both partners have in common and from which both draw according to their needs, dispositions, and moods, without damaging the affective unity created and realized through the initial pact.

In this way the "affect as a whole" is submitted to a kind of external control and rule. To grow and be fully realized, it has to be constantly confirmed by an adequate and mutually identical response. The echo determines the sound. This positive sanction has the value of a permission, the permission to feel and to love. Between the couple S1 and S2 there is a total affective participation based on a magic implication.

"I feel what you feel. You experience what I experience. If you don't feel it, I can't feel it."

Thus fusion leads to confusion. The shared feeling is confused with the individual feeling. The situation thus reflects affective infantile realism.

The result of the formation of an affective whole is the irresponsibility of the feelings even though they originated spontaneously and freely. The subject does not have the right to experience them and manifest them spontaneously and freely of his own initiative because he is much too afraid that an inadequate or discordant answer would ruin his security, because this security is created and guaranteed by the certainty inspired by the mutual unification of the emotions of both partners. Security has become the result of the unity which subjectively has taken on great value.

"I am sure that you love me, because you love me exactly as I love you and because I know that I love you as you love me."

Responsibility is entirely shared and thus cannot be entirely personal. In true reciprocity, the reverse happens; responsibility is shared because it has been assumed previously.

From the genetic point of view, it is wrong to say that affective irresponsibility is the result of the fusion. It is the source of fusion. Inherent from the start in primary realism, it persistently manifests itself in the adult's secondary externalism.

EXAMPLES OF UNIFICATION

"It is wonderful ... Without saying a word ... we know each other's minds . . . have the same ideas, the same wishes, the same desires ..." This is the cheerful statement of a young woman who since her marriage has built up a persistent and passionate friendship for her mother. "We" is "mother and me" and "me and mother." The existence of this "twofold unity" is proof that the marriage is a failure. The identification goes so far that they attempt to breathe together, each making her respiratory rhythm agree with the other. And not only the rhythm but also the amplitude of the thoracic movements. "You see, Doctor, this shows you that we feel the same way about things, have the same feelings, react similarly to similar emotions. Could there be a greater love?"

I have observed two cases of this special kind of participation which I have called "respiratory participation." It is a physiological way of expressing the emotional participation.

One day, both women suffered from the same toothache and went together to the dentist to have their teeth pulled at the same time. The daughter would consent to the extraction only if the mother would have hers out too. But the dentist found nothing. This is a clear example of "participation in pain." Among other organs which react to emotions, the intestinal tract is quite a privileged organ of identification. In one of these two cases one could almost call it a delusional identification and it was the most severe case of such identification that I have observed. It was a "one heart in two breasts" reaction.

This patient, the daughter, had two kinds of demands. First she demanded of herself and her mother (1) that identical feelings, positive or negative, be experienced; (2) that they be expressed in identical ways; (3) that they have the same quality and intensity (which she referred to as "the same amount").

Second, while echoing and sharing were still necessary, they were no longer sufficient. The mother now must also guess the thoughts, desires, and intentions of her beloved daughter. This guessing game complex was a very frequent and highly emotionally invested reaction in these two women. For both the mother and the daughter, the greatest happiness was to "guess first" and surprise the other. Both viewed these intuitions as a consequence and proof of absolute love.

As we see, there exists a curious mixture of demands and renunciations. The patient sacrifices her independence to her mother, but only if the mother also makes the same sacrifice and remains totally dependent upon her daughter.

Another patient, Harriet, depicts in lively terms the type of relationship she has with her husband. The following examples are chosen from a great number of similar ones.

At the movies. She liked the film very much. During the intermission she exclaimed, "It's wonderful, ravishing. This is a great movie. And . . . that scene where the candles go out just as the old man is dying . . . how effective! Don't you think so too?" Her husband replied, "I didn't even notice it." This remark hit Harriet as a dreadful blow. "I suddenly felt like an ice-cold shower had been turned on; all my pleasure was gone. Everything was spoiled, gone, finished. The rest of the movie was indifferent to me. A good movie had become a poor one. I felt sad, depressed, etc. . . ."

Trip to the country. "Sunday we went camping on the banks of a river. Things were better between us . . . I felt I was making progress. The sun, the birds, the river, everything enchanted me. I started to sing . . . then in a moment of pure exuberance, I started to shout with joy . . . I wanted Bob to share in my joy, to sing with me . . . but he didn't even react, didn't even pay any attention. And then as usual, I suddenly got all sad. The veil had fallen; my happiness was destroyed.

"Sometimes, instead of getting sad when he doesn't react, I make a violent scene. I know that after these quarrels he is crushed, like a whipped puppy. But it puts him in the same state that I am in (sadness, depression) and that is what I want. It seems to appease me to see him feel like me . . . and then the joy comes back . . . if he follows my example and imitates me, everything becomes happy again . . . then everything is all right. Otherwise the quarreling starts all over again . . . and so on."

These sudden leaps from the euphoric to the depressive states are characteristic of a total extraversion of affectivity. Externalism could not be greater. One principle remains foreign to all these patients and those who participate in their manifest affects. They do not realize that what consciousness experiences spontaneously and what thought creates fully and with autonomy is more valuable than what they attempt to instigate in others. Months of analysis are necessary before these patients realize the wisdom of this principle.

They have remained at the imitative stage described by Baldwin (see Section 3). In one sense the child discovers himself while imitating others, but he also attributes to himself the behavior which he observes in others and in his object, particularly. Basing this attitude on the principles of genetic psychology, we could call it the "Baldwinian complex." It is hard therapeutic work to destroy its foundation for it is extremely deeply rooted.

65. Anxiety and the Need for the Absolute

We still must review briefly the role played by anxiety in the formation of the need for the absolute. The relationship between affect and concept is important and close, and everything leads us to believe that it originates in childhood. I will limit myself to a summary of the considerations developed in the preceding paragraphs (especially in Section 62).

In the adult, anxiety presupposes a horror of the relative. Anxiety is the cause of the schism, specifically of the abandonee's, between logic and speculative faculties, on one hand, and affective functions on the other. The latter blind judgment on one particular point: the logic of interpersonal relationships. Anxiety is the prototype of the reaction to the loss of the absolute. Its intensity is the best measure of the intensity of the infantile need to see this feeling absolutely satisfied.

Conclusion. The principal result of this body of prelogical concepts is a clearer and more coherent picture of the abandonee's affective life as well as of its double regulation through affect and concept. The deeper study of the regulating mechanisms leads us to consider these concepts as a kind of intellectual accompaniment of the affective reactions. Affect nourishes thought. Magic is inherent in the nature of feeling but contingent to the nature of thinking.

CHAPTER NINE

RECEPTION AND PRESENCE
SEPARATION AND ABSENCE
THEIR AFFECTIVE FUNCTION AND VALUE

INTRODUCTION

Reception (or welcome) and presence, separation and absence are four "social events" everybody has experienced and felt to be important. They can be considered from different viewpoints. There is, for example, a clear-cut difference between a conventional and polite reception and a passionate welcome. The gradations are affective. A social, even a purely spatial, event has become an essentially sentimental and emotional event. The affective function and value of these events will be the subject of this chapter.

It is logical to start with reception. Affective reception can be defined as a certain way of welcoming dictated by the feelings of the welcomer for the welcomed. Inspired by these feelings, the manner of welcoming usually mirrors them perfectly. Sentimental individuals demand such displays. To some of them the whole affective relationship of any one time initially depends upon this reception, and any defect felt in the welcome can alter or break the relationship. Among the four mentioned events, reception is not the least important.

There are many kinds of affective reception—as many as there are people who welcome each other with the many shadings of positive and negative feelings which they have for each other. The behavior of one individual toward another who

245

functions as a partner is always inspired and regulated by feelings. The way in which a person does or does not react to the departure or the return of another individual is the best indication of his real feelings, be they manifest or hidden. His reaction is a measure of the value, quality and nature of these feelings.

The topic of the following paragraph will be a particular category of acceptance especially valued by abandonees: the special "elective"[1] welcome.

66. Special "Elective" Welcome as a Demand

The demand for a special welcome is common in abandonees of both sexes. If it cannot be fully satisfied, the disappointment provokes practically identical reactions in both men and women and can thus be considered to be independent of the subject's sex.

In the following passages, I will present in a condensed form a series of mishaps experienced by some of my patients. As they all share the same psychoneurotic reaction, I will use only one name for all of them.

Mr. A. is a very busy Parisian and works hard all day. Living in the suburbs, he has a fairly long distance to cover before he reaches home at the end of his working day. He comes home very tired and full of worries. He feels inferior to his employer. At the end of every week he thinks of quitting, but every Monday sees him punctually back on the job. As he reaches his house, he has but one wish: to be nicely received by his wife. Nothing could be more legitimate than this compensatory need. Crossing the threshold he hopes for a warm welcome, a kind

---

[1] Translator's note. The terms "election" and "elective" as used in the English language do not have the sense given them by the author. They have therefore been translated according to their meaning by using other terms, such as "unique," "special," "chosen one," "choice," etc.

look, a tender gesture and a long kiss. This is his stated expectation, consistent with the logical form of marital relationships. Actually, deeper down his demand has a quite different objective.

To become fully effective, the gesture of welcome must convey a hidden meaning. It has to assume a very special "quality" which will be a proof of the unique and exclusive love of his wife. The latter must reserve the quality of this welcome for her husband alone. Mr. A. refuses to be welcomed in the same way as she welcomes his father-in-law, his uncles, brothers-in-law, or even his son. The critical moment has the value of a test. Upon it depends happiness or unhappinesss.

As he opens the door, or preferably when he is at the garden entrance, Mr. A. expects his wife to put down everything, to run out to meet him in a way which will give him an infallible token of her special and "unique" love. If she correctly fulfills all these conditions, her reception has a magic effect. It dispels worries, relieves tiredness, eases tension, and relaxes his whole body. A radiant smile erases the wrinkles. In brief, by a magic touch a dysphoric state turns into euphoria. This is his best antidote for anxiety. All the way home Mr. A. becomes increasingly anxious, tormented by doubts. He wonders if the welcome will be "special" or not. He has never been able to confess to his wife the exact object of his demand—which is actually that of an abandoned child.

"If my wife welcomes me as I wish she would, strange as it seems, I recover all my self-confidence. My fears and scruples disappear as if by magic. [The term is well chosen.] My life takes on new meaning. Instead of wanting to quit the job I feel like telling my boss off, but good. And if he goes on bothering me, to put him in his place for good, etc. . . ."

Once more it is evident that the magic power of the "special" reception is manifested by an instantaneous and complete re-valuation of the self which takes place along with a return of internal security. At the same time, the boss loses his role as an object of negative comparison. Suddenly the patient is able to compare himself positively with his employer.

The preceding considerations are sufficient to reveal the secret of this tremendous power. Such happy effects explain why Mr. A. is constantly watching for proofs from his wife that he is the "chosen one." It is not by accident that all the Mr. A's complain bitterly that they had a cold, sharp mother, a hard and authoritarian mother—a mother who could not accept them. Psychiatrists find that there are too many mothers who seem to ignore, not only the value and importance of this phenomenon of acceptance, but even its existence. As an excuse, they most often say that they have so many other things to do. This is a good excuse, but hardly adequate when the alternative is the development of neurosis.

The husbands of Mr. A's type have a tendency to "maternalize" their wives, and if the wife enters the game and consents to this substitution, they tend to idealize her through contrast or compensation. Unfortunately, between ideal and reality, between ideal mother and real wife, all deviations are possible and inevitable. Each divergence can become a source of disappointments badly tolerated by the husbands who are abandonees.

In this respect, the wives fall into two categories; those who allow themselves to be maternalized and like this role to which they were predestined by nature, and those who refuse. In the first case, the marriage can be harmonious, with the sexual life receding into the background. Masculinity in the husband is not too important in the union. In the second case, the marriage fares badly. (For further development of this theme, see Section 70.)

Thus far we can make one general remark. The most specific characteristic of these men is their intense and irreversible fixation on their mothers or mother substitutes. At all times, they tend to compare the wife with the mother, for good and bad. This antithetic game gives rise successively to compliments or recriminations. If the wife is a good psychologist, she will understand. Nonetheless this is an important area of disagreement and quarrels. The second one is no less serious.

The second danger lies in relation to the children, and the more children there are, the greater the danger. They are innocently predestined to the role of their father's rivals and therefore to become a source of jealousy. The mother has to manage this as best she can, but her role is a most frustrating one. Her natural inclination to devote body and soul to her children is challenged and even denied. She is not allowed to fully express her motherly love. If she does so, her gestures, favors, and care are interpreted as so many acts of infidelity.

Thus we are back to the recurrent theme. The husband is jealous of his children because he spontaneously interprets his wife's "offenses" as signs of *preference*.

The suspicion becomes a conviction because he confuses the real conditions with which a young mother has to cope with the intentions he imagines. The more these are dreaded, the more they impose themselves upon his mind and gain in certainty. Thus, an obsession becomes a conviction when it is invested with infantile affects. The affects transform the "fear-ideas" into absolute beliefs. As soon as the absolute belief in a preference has arisen, a chain of axioms will be released with an inexorableness that no logical thinking will be able to stop: preference—sharing—withdrawal of love—loss of love object—abandonment. Anxiety is created and will in turn produce its own effects.

The husband who has been betrayed by his own child can choose between two alternatives: the active way of revenge and violence, or the passive way of withdrawal, sulking, or masochistic regression. His temperament will decide his choice. Whatever his decision, extreme difficulties for the young mother will result and can only increase her troubled adjustment as wife and mother.

67. The Three Functions of the "Special Reception"

If the abandonee does not receive a "special welcome," this means to him that he is not his object's "chosen one" or that he has forfeited the uniqueness of this position because of separation. Separation invariably has a traumatic effect. Inversely, warm acceptance is truly beneficial, re-creates hope previously shattered by doubts, and brings back *asphaleia*.

Acceptance provides two proofs secretly expected by the abandonee, one concerning the past, one the future.

First, it shows that the bond has not been destroyed by the always threatening separation. Having been well received, the subject is at once sure that he has not ceased to occupy first place in the heart and mind of his object; that the latter's feelings have lost nothing of their uniqueness; that they have retained their special nature.

Second, this special nature is a proof that the tie is solidly established for the future. The abandonee can thus count on its duration. He is happy to be assured that separation will be unable to interrupt the continuity of the relationship. This knowledge is a precious safeguard to him and he is reassured that inevitable future absences will also be innocuous. In principle, the way of welcoming reveals the way of "being absent": that is, of remaining present through absence, or available despite separation.

For the abandonee, every separation, every distance is an ordeal which is difficult for him to endure. He demands that the method, the techniques of separation have the same qualities, the same reassuring tones as the way of reuniting. If the latter has to be characterized by sincere joy, the former has to reveal a no less sincere regret, a no less special and unique sorrow; such manifestations will then create security. The slightest coldness in a farewell must mean "good riddance" and an ever so slightly cool or moody welcome will create profound insecurity.

For these subjects separation and reception must take place in the same emotional climate. This alone guarantees security and continuity in the relationship. One of the abandonee's essential requests is that his object be constantly available. No third person, no event, neither space nor time, should come between them.

Reunion and welcome are far more than the simple re-establishment of a spatial contact. Rather than a physical fact they constitute a psychological event. On the level of logic, the reunion obviously ends and cancels separation. However, on the level of prelogic, its action is deeper; it is magic. *It suppresses absence.* This is the secret of the "bewitching power" of the "special" welcome.

Usually the object unconsciously plays his role as a magician. It is always dangerous to be endowed with magic power, but even more dangerous to be unaware of it. For example, how many among our patients' mothers all over the world are aware of their prestige, a prestige bringing more obligations than liberties? Can they draw the necessary educational conclusions? And all the absent-minded husbands of waiting wives? Actually the victims of persons obsessed by such absolute feelings usually sense and foresee many things but remain unable to explain them clearly. Their lives are spent in being caught napping. It is important to reveal to them the existence and subtle actions of the prelogical axioms which are so often used by their child, husband or wife. When I ask to see these relatives at the beginning of therapy, I often terminate the interview with a bit of good advice: "Be especially careful with your hello's and good-bye's."

Conclusion. The "special welcome" has three functions: It suppresses absence. It assures continuity. It safeguards the duration of the relationship despite time and space. Thus it maintains the indissolubility of the union.

68. Unquestionable Proofs of the Uniqueness of Choice

Uniqueness of choice and indissolubility are the foremost means of maintaining security and harmony. To the patient they have almost an awe-inspiring wondrous value. Distance and absence exist no more if a third condition is fulfilled.

Just as the manner of being absent or of welcoming, the way of "being present" has to be unique and special. In the presence of the object, especially in front of others, the subject requests unquestionable proofs. These proofs consist in facial expressions, glances, gestures, and the thousand signs, serious or amusing, evident or secret, which form the "code language" familiar to all lovers. Everything depends on the tone and the warmth of this attitude.

These certain signs, in turn, have three functions. They serve (1) to dispel the fear of competition and rivalry; (2) to prevent the trial of sharing; (3) to weaken the uncertainty created by neutral intervals, the "dead-spots" or the cooling of love such as time alone can bring about. They prevent love from degenerating into a sum of habits and pure conventions.

On the other hand, we all know that there is a way of being present without being so, or a way of being absent while present. These are attitudes which produce anxiety in the abandonee.

69. "False Presence" or Unaffective Presence

Most people are probably dimly aware of the existence of one factor which so frequently and evidently hurts and disappoints our patients. Much of their anxiety and unhappiness is caused by a certain way their objects have of being "falsely present" or of being here but not really present.

The elements of this kind of relationship are quite difficult to describe clearly. A few definitions are necessary.

In Section 66, the existence and action of a very particular functional relationship have been described. We noted that the special kind of reunion and reception is closely related to the way of being absent or of being present. In the eyes of the subject, this means of course, that the warmth of the reception or of the reunion is an infallible proof that the feelings toward him have not varied during the separation. On the magical level, there has simply been no real absence. Space has lost the power to destroy the affective tie. Feelings strong enough to have created such a unique relationship are more powerful than space. Since no true absence was experienced, there has only been a "false absence."

In a "false absence" one remains united in heart and thought. The subject has only one aspiration: that the object's only wish, in spite of all distracting influences, be to see him again as soon as possible and that he live only with this expectation.

On the other hand, a "true" absence means a weakening, a

dispersal or disappearance of the feelings and restores to space all its frightful power.

From the functional point of view, "false absence" does not damage the feelings of security in any way, whereas "true" absence weakens and even destroys them. If a subject is really the "chosen one," the object is always present . . . even if he forgets to telephone. Indeed phone calls exert a magic power. They suppress space. They are true signs, not to be doubted. For a similar reason, telegrams are favored over letters. They abolish time or, at least, waiting. To the abandonee waiting is a source of doubt and insecurity which is borne with difficulty. For a subject who doubts that he is the "chosen one," an object who is leaving is already absent. "True" absence is characterized by its devaluating power and is a mortal blow to internal security.

Similar definitions can be applied to two corresponding modes of presence. In "false presence," the object is here—but not really present. He is here in the flesh but not in the spirit. "What, of whom is he thinking? He does not seem to enjoy my presence . . . nor even his own." There is neither union nor reunion, only contiguity. There is no true presence. Even though present, the object is absent, and this kind of absence can be more harmful and anxiety-producing than true absence. To the subject, being present means lavishing marks of tenderness and affection, giving proofs of love. This is the sole aim of being present. Disappointed patients will state: "It's really not worth while! We might as well separate." The subject would rather have a true absence for it will be less painful.

It is true that the unaffective presence causes more harm than a true absence following a frank separation, courageously accepted. Of the two evils, "absence in presence" is worse. In true affective absence there can sometimes be a certain, even pleasant presence. The certainty of having been "chosen" preserves contact while unaffective presence rudely interrupts it, and negates the choice. False presence exasperates and depresses certain abandonees who, on the contrary, are calmed by true absence. During the latter, they can freely withdraw and brood over their misfortune. They are exempt from having to seek revenge and thus are free to relax and regain their inner peace.

The characteristic function of the object's presence is to arouse needs, to stir up desires; false presence does not escape this function. But while awakening these desires and needs, a false presence cannot satisfy them or leaves the most imperious ones unsatisfied. Exasperation and a sort of obsession with frustration follows, even though the object is not really ill-tempered. It is enough that he be unaffective. Too many children suffer from this obsessive feeling.

The very infantile affectivity of the abandonee leads him to confuse unaffective presence and true abandonment; and may even lead him to view it as the false abandonment, discussed in this book more, and painful than a true one. I have often observed this, especially in certain children who seem to have suffered more from an unaffective and always "falsely present" mother (perhaps father) than other children who have had to put up with true abandonment or a definitive absence irrevocably established.

Unaffectivity suppresses the reassuring function of presence at the very time it makes presence more desirable, more imperatively requested. The subject seems condemned to the torture of Tantalus. The unaffective mother openly betrays her mission, whereas the absent mother does not fulfill hers, which is very different.

It is characteristic that a "false presence" will block the realization of a happy relation between the action of the object and the needs of the subject. It prevents or destroys intimate harmony. Thus frustrated, the subject is rarely able to reverse the roles. He lacks the strength to do so, or does not even think of it, even though this reversal could be his salvation.

On one hand we have a purely material or physical presence which can be reduced to a succession of motor acts and impersonal words. On the other hand there is affective and thus effective presence. The person is here for you. These two modes are radically opposed as to function as well as values. Certain precocious children soon discover this opposition without clearly understanding it; suffering from it they feel it intuitively. And their suffering is all the more acute because it is powerless. On the contrary, an adequate relation between their basic needs and the attitude of the persons in charge of their care is predicated on the true presence of these persons. This is so true that a true presence can be sufficient for some infants. It acts independently of care and signs of love. These little ones confuse presence and tenderness. The inhibited attitude of certain adults is based on this confusion and maintained by it.

There are as many types of affective presence as there are different types of mothers and children. There are as many types of "nonaffective" presence as there are mothers and educators who are "not quite here" and whose children suffer from abandonment. "Nonaffective" presence can assume at least three forms:

The "purely material presence": body care, toileting, dressing, medication, hygiene, supervision, etc.

The "cold presence": wry, cold, silent, at times directly frustrating and painful (punishment, etc.).

The "dutiful presence": the person is there only because it is her moral, educational and physical duty to the child. The accomplishment of this duty is the sole justification for being with the child. The material (or physical) results of the work accomplished are the only things that really matter; its moral effects on the subject are evaluated only according to whether or not they fall in line with the object's principles. The emotional results of such a presence remain ununderstood, if thought of at all; or what little understanding there may be is a mere by-product.

At the basis of all these "nonaffective" attitudes we find complete disregard for the subject's needs. If it concerns a child one could say: it is not proper for the educator ever to worry about or even to be aware of the child's need for security and ever to let it interfere with the proper course of education. I must limit myself to this brief description; but it is indeed difficult for an analyst to refrain from always going back to the "prototypical" situations; the patients themselves constantly refer us to the original sources of all their troubles. This disregard for the child's need for security is at the basis of the neurosis of abandonment and of some especially deep-seated inferiority complexes. It cannot be overstressed that a child with normal needs who does not feel himself truly loved, not really his mother's "chosen one," whose mother is unaware that she is ungiving and unloving, that such a child will not be able to acquire any sense of his own value.

The reactions of abandonees of all age groups to a "false" or "nonaffective" presence are as varied as they are harmful. Generally speaking they can be divided into active and passive reactions. Among the active forms we find the particularly harmful recrimination complex previously described. When the object is by nature egocentric and nonaffective, he cannot understand the recriminations of the subject, can conceive neither of their cause nor of their function or meaning. He tends to react by defending himself or striking back. People who are not really present are always very susceptible when blamed, as it often happens, for lack of attention, kindness or even elementary politeness. In these cases a new vicious circle is soon created.

A frequent form of passive reaction is sulking as a demonstration or way of getting back at the object. "You think you are giving me everything; well, I will show you that you aren't giving me anything or at least not what I need most. In order to prove it I too will hold back everything and give nothing." Many sulky abandonees have a very sure instinct, an acute intuition for a "false presence." This is demonstrated by their impulse to flee, to separate from the "falsely present" person, to withdraw into themselves. The presence of the object having become unbearable, they bring about separation and absence as if true insecurity were preferable to false security. Finally, in despair, all there is left to the sulking abandonee is to look in himself for some security. This is an attempt at reestablishing self-esteem, but unfortunately an attempt which is bound to fail. It is nonetheless true that the sulking and withdrawing individual really prefers a true absence to a make-believe presence.

Other forms of reactions with a predominance of inhibition, such as anxiety, fearfulness, and silent suffering should also be mentioned. Other more active reactions include the search for a more satisfactory object and attachment to him, and flight from the family. Further description would be too long for this discussion.

Let me conclude on a more pleasant note. At the end of the day, father comes home, tired, nervous, and gloomy. After mumbling the usual few words he slumps in his easy chair with pipe and newspaper. This is not the way his five-year-old daughter, Arleen, wants it. She cannot tolerate the "false presence" of her daddy, her "prince," as she calls him. Mother is in the kitchen and Arleen cautiously circles around the "prince's" chair slowly coming closer to make her presence known. Her presence, charged with all the loving admiration she has for her father, is as true and "affective" as the mute presence of her father is "false" and "nonaffective." Soon she begins a little courting. Her object grumbles; his only wish is to be left alone with his newspaper. However, this little game has occurred before and follows a set pattern. In the last act, flatteries, tender gestures and nice words will bring the "falsely present" father back to his little daughter. He finally is defeated and everything ends with kisses and a little dance. Arleen well knows that she is the one weakness of her loving father. So often absent he is finally present, and very present indeed. Mother is still in the kitchen and Arleen is assured that she is the chosen one. This is a victory with all the security and self-esteem it brings. A child's happiness is summed up by these three words: victory, security and self-esteem.

70. DIFFERENT TYPES OF PARTNERS

It often happens that an abandonee, either through perspicacity or blindness, chooses another abandonee as a partner. Theoretically, in these cases, the roles are reversible. In practice they are at times reversed; at other times, the two partners refuse to play the game of reciprocity with an exchange of functions based on their mutual insecurity. A periodic reversal of roles can become a precious and unexpected factor of harmony between the two partners. We can call this a mechanism of "double insurance" or "mutual reassurance." The existence of this mechanism implies that the partners have remained at the stage of procuring security from exogenous sources; but this "leveling at the base" allows them to understand each other through a mutual intuition of each other's feelings. If they have chosen each other without knowing about their complexes, they soon realize them and communicate intuitively. However, the real motives for this communion remain hidden. The joy of reassuring the other is only equalled by the joy of being reassured by him. The pride derived from the active attitude compensates for the humiliation of the passive attitude. Thus a certain degree of equilibrium can be established and maintained. In a married couple, a normal or only mildly disturbed sexual life contributes to the stabilization based on two concurring forms of neurosis. A remarkable capacity for identification or affective participation is the rule in these couples, so much so that the partners themselves and the people in their environment consider these spontaneous processes as indicative of a deep and lasting love. Practically this opinion is true, even though it is theoretically wrong. When two narcissisms are confronted, so to speak, they can mutually neutralize each other with the help of some intuition and much good will. However, they can also affront each other, and collisions will be inevitable if one of the partners has an irritable disposition, is more vindictive or aggressive than the other. In the end, the latter will become tired and, if not irritable himself, will resort to the technique of "false presence" as a means of defense. And the unhappy outcome will be inevitable.

"False presence" is contagious; if one partner resorts to it, the other will also. This is his only resource and there is no better way of defending himself or of counterattacking. Then we have two "absentees" confronting each other and often condemned by fate to remain with each other. Both expect the same from the other. Nothing weighs more heavily, is more painful, more devaluating and security-destroying than these situations of "mutual expectancy." Marital life becomes based more and more upon two reactive negativisms. The first is reactive to the second and vice versa, but both have the same function: to retaliate, more out of despair than out of hostility. It is a demonstration similar to sulking. In order to demonstrate one needs to be present, therefore the need arises for a double "false presence." For such situations there is hardly any remedy. Only periodic separations can occasionally avoid disaster. Two actual absences are more tolerable than two "false presences." The two members of the couple are already disunited. They live together but are already divorced.[2] The communion of which they dreamed has turned into a "co-separation." The nervous and emotional balance of the children is badly threatened. The older children, if they cannot function as a uniting factor, have a most difficult position. The younger ones breathe a poisonous atmosphere full of abandonment. They suffer without being able to understand. They are faced with a falsified and vicious image of marital relationship and are pervaded by it. They finally come to believe that this is the normal type of marriage, the natural and universal way of family life because this is what they see at home, acted out by their parents. Certain children, however, rather than accepting this sad and false example, react by creating by contrast for themselves the opposite and positive ideal. Their tendency to draw away from the family facilitates this task. They are truly present only outside the family circle; inside it they imitate their parents and take refuge in "false presence"—or their rooms. There are actually families in which nobody is present. The fact of living under the same roof is the only link between its members.

In such circumstances well-balanced children are rare and a progressive development is far from the rule. Certain children side with one or the other parent who, consciously or not, en-

---

[2] Psychoanalysis has often been accused of making divorces. In reality it more often unveils already existing divorces than it provokes new ones. To reveal a divorce before it reaches the court is to fulfill an honest mission and is certainly not the least successful means to prevent a psychic divorce from ending in a legal one.

courages this. A mother who is never present for her husband, makes great efforts to be all the more present for her children. She transfers all her affectivity to them and attempts to tie them to herself. The betrayed feminine instinct seeks compensation in maternity. For the child, especially for the daughter, an exclusively maternal affection entirely dissociated from paternal love is a source of many disturbances and conflicts. The reverse dissociation, though less frequent, is no less dangerous. In both cases, the child is predisposed to an unsolved oedipus complex.

In these chapters on adults it would be inappropriate to expand further on these most regrettable family constellations. I wish only to point out that they are a common source of neurosis of abandonment in the child. If husband and wife maintain an attitude of "false presence" toward each other and tolerate it, this is not a mere hazard of marriage but an attitude due to a premarital and very old neurosis. Most probably this has been a neurosis of abandonment, which can pass from parents to children, from generation to generation. The "virus" is transmittable, and the illness is the most widespread "family neurosis." At the source of all cases of neurosis of abandonment I have observed, I have found such an abnormal family situation.

Conclusion. "False presence" of the object is not a lesser evil than actual absence. "False presence" is a source of frustration and a sign of abandonment. It starves while it increases the appetite.

It can also serve as a defense mechanism in any form of neurosis. It is used as a weapon and leads the two partners to either one of two alternatives: either they separate and try to reunite by writing to each other and finally talk and explain. Or they stay together, fight more and more and draw further apart. The fate of the couple and the children lie in this difficult choice.

CHAPTER TEN

FROM LIFE TO DEATH AND FROM DEATH TO LIFE

71. DEATH FANTASIES AND INDISSOLUBLE BONDS

Only a minority of human beings is indifferent to the prospect of death—and "I will die like everything alive in nature" is far from being the abandonee's conception.[1] The abandonee is so intensely haunted by the idea of separation because he equates it with disappearance and disappearance with death. His anxiety about death is part of his fear of separation. For the abandonee, perpetual separation is a painful experience through which he has lived at least once, or believes he has, which is even worse. We know now that the imagined experience is even more cruel than the real experience. Both escape the logic of relationships, and for the abandonee's prelogical mind, so does death. Separation from the object implies his death or the death of the subject himself . . . death of one or the other. In order to fight against this feeling of mourning and to triumph over the grief caused by solitude, the subject invents fantasies and abandons himself to them in the worst moments of his depression.

If on the level of real experience separation is a kind of death, on the level of fantasy such a confusion is corrected or dispelled. To die is a way of avoiding separation, or better of never parting any more. Death fantasies with such a function of reparation, compensation, and consolation are extremely frequent at critical

[1] Analysis shows us that this indifference, or better this serenity, goes with an absence of guilt feelings. It increases progressively as the infantile superego abandons his pseudo morality so that the moral conscience can establish its own positions.

moments in analysis. As we see, their function is of a magic nature. These daydreams provide us with first-hand documents about the abandonee's affective ego psychology in periods of crisis. These fantasies show a remarkable gradation of supernatural conceptions. While absorbed with them, the subject completely loses sight of the concept of natural death as an end to life. Clinically, the common mechanism of these fantasies consists in a sudden loss of security followed by a loss of self-esteem. This is the one element of unity among the great diversity of these fantasies. Here is a summary of the most typical ones.

FANTASIES OF THE FIRST DEGREE

The general theme is separation or loss of the object following the appearance of a rival. The compensatory process consists in imagining the death of the object and the rival. I will here condense the essential elements of many scenes into one episode.

One evening Mr. A. comes home depressed; this is his usual way of reacting to worries and fatigue. Having opened the door he finds himself in the dark. His first shock is that nobody is there. Somewhat like a robber he wanders about the house. Supper is not ready, his slippers are not in place. Not only is it dark, he is now lonely. This is a second shock. Desperate and angry, he finally finds his wife upstairs. The baby is sick, the doctor has not yet come. The anxious young mother does not pay her husband due homage as she should. There is no "special" welcome, in fact, no welcome at all. This is the third shock. Feeling nearly cast out, the husband at first tries to reassure his unfaithful wife :"You worry far too much. It is not so bad, why such a fuss? . . . it is not good for the baby." And he thinks: "When *I* am ill, you never worry so much." During supper he does not open his mouth. He is unable to express either recriminations or complaints. They are, so to say, poured into his silence. He feels oppressed. After the meal he withdraws to his study. Gloomy thoughts flash through his mind. Suddenly they are all condensed into one death fantasy. "Through neglect or error, I have poisoned my wife and her son. I appear before the Court." And then he imagines a long scene where at times he provokes and insults the judges, and at other times, he is humble and tries to soften them through his tears. In such apparently murderous fantasies, despair and revenge are closely mixed, the first justifying the second.

Fantasies of Incarceration

Be the imagined crime real or symbolic, this daydreamer is thrown into prison. "I see myself alone in my cell. I am tremendously relieved. It is like a complete deliverance. I no longer need to kill myself for my wife and child. It is high time that somebody should take care of me . . . etc." This fantasy of incarceration is not a rare one. Its symbolism has a double aspect. First, prison means absolute security; it abolishes struggles and defeats. Comparisons become impossible. There is a striking contrast between this security recovered through absolute irresponsibility and the insecurity and total loss of self-esteem provoked by the loss of the object. Second, material care is assured in prison. This certainty makes the subject overlook the inadequacy of the care. The prison becomes a symbol of maternal solicitude. "Let *her* take care of the baby as much as she wants. *I* have my warden. He is really very nice, understands my misfortune and has special attentions and favors for me. We are good friends, etc. . . ." The nice warden has made up for the abandonment by the bad wife.

FANTASIES OF THE SECOND DEGREE

Double Murder or Double Suicide

There are numerous variations. "My husband (or my mother, my wife, my son) has committed suicide. I then imagine that I kill myself too." These fantasies are rarely so simple and so crude. There is always something vague, mysterious and sinister about them. Strange ceremonies are substituted for the usual funerals. Some patients lose themselves in details, others avoid them. But from the way they tell these "stories," it is evident that they have stopped reliving them. The effort of telling them alone has relieved the patient.

True dreams usually go along with these fantasies and exaggerate their magic character. Here is such a dream from a patient who never really had his mother because she was always "falsely present." "It is my father's funeral and my own at the same time. We both are present at our own burial. We are both buried the same day with great pomp. The atmosphere between us is very peaceful and even affectionate. I can see him, grave and moved, with his long white hair." The father had had such white hair; and his death had been a great shock to his son.

The main theme of these fantasies is the double death of object and subject. Their deeper meaning is not that of a crime but of a solution. At their origin we always find abandonment of some kind, experienced or imagined by the subject (partial choice, rejection, sharing, separation, etc.). It may happen that the object shares his feelings and devotion with the subject and a beloved person who has died recently or long ago. This kind of rivalry is very badly tolerated by the subject who feels completely disarmed. His only resource is to fantasy his own death. In heaven there are no more differences. Everybody is loved the same. This is what educators teach children. In confusing himself with the dead rival the subject suppresses the rival. To live on earth and have his rival in heaven puts the subject in a state of total inferiority and powerlessness.

After having lost her mother, a young woman in an uninterrupted series of dreams goes back to live with the beloved deceased, takes her room, wears her clothes, sees her belongings. She identifies with the dead and thus suppresses her grief and separation. In other dreams she herself dies.[2]

The ultimate goal of the double death is to annul separation; on this infantile level of thought, love and death in no way exclude each other. Union in death is believed to be indissoluble and eternal. Thus such a fantasy brings about the realization of the indissolubility of the bond which is the deepest wish of any abandonee. Double death transposes double life to eternity, to the absolute. It relieves the relationship from the heavy mortgage of relativity. Far from being a drama, it ends the real drama. Death, like love, has its magic. Love is more certain in death than in life, at least, more certain to last. It is an idealization of earthly love, which is so precarious, so threatened by relativity and dissolution.

This is the theme of double death which certain subjects who suffer from attacks of depression are prone to cultivate. They want this fantasy to repair an irreparable evil, the impossibility of an absolute understanding between two human beings. Or perhaps this evil lies in the impossible desire for such an understanding, the nostalgia for perfect love. Which is true I do not know. In any case, the fantasy originates at the point where reality and wish clash, it is an attempt to shape reality according to the ideal. In this world an ideal life together is impossible to realize if it is to be like the complete unity conceived by the

---

[2] The taboo about the room of a deceased person has a similar meaning. Clothes, objects, and furniture must be left as they were and in the same order as before the death.

child. Thus death together in its deepest sense compensates for
the impossibility of a complete unity between two human beings.
Such a unity is illusory in this world, but could it not be possible
in the next?

The following dream is that of a thirty-three-year-old Parisian
woman:

"A strange funeral reaches the Place des Martyrs. It is a
woman's funeral . . . or a great lady's. I see the corpse lying on
a stretcher, but it strikes me that it is carried by eight pallbearers
instead of the usual four." The theme of double death is here
realized through the use of numbers. If four pallbearers mean
one corpse, eight evidently means two corpses. The end of the
nightmare proves this. "Things change. I see a big open hole
in the ground. At the moment when the dead woman is thrown
into the grave, she changes into a doll; and blood comes out."
We later ascertained that the doll represented the patient as a
child.

72. ASSISTING AT ONE'S OWN FUNERAL

This is the most typical of the abandonee's fantasies and
reveals best the power of his unfulfilled wishes.

"I am supposed to be dead. The funeral is going to start. With
much emotion I visualize all the scenes and observe with great
interest the behavior of all people present. I watch especially the
feelings and reactions of . . ." (This person will be the actual
and most important object or representative of older authority
objects such as mother, father or their substitutes, husband, or
wife, or favorite child.) "I fix my attention on the way he expresses his grief. I see his deeply altered features. The crucial
moment is when he bursts into tears, incapable of mastering his
emotion, his grief, unable to be comforted. In his grief in front
of my deathbed, my coffin, or my grave, I see the proof of his

love which he had hidden from me or of which he had been unaware. Henceforth I am sure, even if he does not know it or does not want to admit it, I was (I am) *the one who counts most for him.*"

Thus the attention of the subject is selectively focused on the affective reactions of the object. It is clear that the aim of such fantasies is to put the love of the object (or objects in the family) on trial: a hard trial which will prove this love's quality, strength and value. And is there a better way for demonstrating this value than in the unquestionable signs of posthumous "choice"? This experience is decisive. It ends gnawing doubts, dispels illusions, annuls disappointments.

"Finally I will know where I stand. I will know if I am really, sincerely and deeply loved or if my life is of no value to anybody, of no value at all." This value is measured by the intensity of the regrets caused by the subject's death, by the number of tears shed.

This fantasy thus has a double effect. On the one hand it overcomes the feeling of powerlessness with all its obsessions of injustice which lead to bitter revindication; on the other hand, it abolishes the feeling of uncertainty and insecurity. It goes even further in that it suppresses the loss of security and value caused by the certainty of being unloved and unchosen. The favorable outcome of the trial, its unhoped-for or rather too-much-hoped-for issue abolishes anxiety. In this respect the fantasy is in no way deathly and destructively aggressive; it is essentially compensatory, restoring and liberating. It does not have the meaning of a sad ending but the value of a new start, a return to happiness. It owes this value to its fundamental function which is to restore the feeling of security and its inseparable companion, valorization.

"From the way I am mourned I can finally measure my value."

This is the axiom used by the abandonee. This idea or this wish becomes an absolute conviction as long as the fantasy lasts, as long as its contents produce comforting and reviving emotions. But what comes later? The fantasy will have to be analyzed to help the patient face the painful elements of reality. But as long as it lasts it is at least able to free the subject from his most anxiety-producing affects, the same affects that have disrupted his emotional balance.

Thus the fantasy exerts paradoxical functions. In the first sense: it *realizes and confirms the subject's position as the "chosen one"* in a way that is posthumous only in appearance, in that it tries to influence the future by making it less unhappy than the past. The most thrilling moment when the so-called corpse drops into his grave does not have the meaning of a definitive separation through death—to imagine this as an irreparable misfortune would be contrary to the affective prelogic of the abandonee.

In the second sense, it is a very powerful mechanism to increase security. The reading of Sophocles' *Electra* is more convincing in this respect than the modern textbooks of psychology. This will be elaborated in later paragraphs.

In summary, we do not deal with a death wish but with a desire to live; not with a funeral but with a rebirth. These fantasies create an intimate tie between love and rebirth. They show the power of the eternal over the ephemeral, of the certain over the uncertain, of the finished over the unfinished, of perfection over imperfection, of the absolute over the relative.

We could not dream of more clever fantasies. They are inspired by the notion of eternal life as conceived in its original affective meaning of eternal love.

73. THE POSSIBLE NEGATIVE FUNCTION OF
DEATH FANTASIES

Let us consider a different case of disappointed or false love. Either the subject has antagonized the object through his excessive recriminations or through his exasperating sulking which solves nothing. Or the object has chosen someone else, out of opposition or lassitude, or to reaffirm his own natural right to become a subject himself and thus to enjoy the benefits of being the "chosen one." Whatever the reasons are for this misfortune, the subject considers the object lost. He is desperate but at times also angry. This ambivalence inspires unpleasant thoughts, wishes for revenge or reprisals. These cruel disappointments awaken the dormant instinct for retaliation. Restored to its rights, the primitive justice of the talion is introduced into the fantasy life and becomes the predominant factor. The fantasied burial of oneself becomes a veritable funeral novel:

"As you have abandoned me, so I will abandon you."

"After my death and through it, you will finally realize the magnitude of my misfortune, the amount of my suffering, and the greatness of your fault."

"My misfortune becomes yours; I leave my suffering to you."

"See now, what it was like, how hard things have been. You will only be able to understand my suffering when you too experience it."

"And from now on, you will regret what you did to me all your life. May your remorse last to your dying day. This will be only fair punishment for you."

REMARKS ON A MACABRE PHOBIA

The fantasy of one's own funeral considered in its favorable aspect has its exact antithesis in the phobia of being buried alive. Its object or content is apparent at once. It is a terrifying vision directly inspired by primary anxiety. The subject sees himself buried but still alive. He still is breathing in his closed coffin. He expects the ordeal of thirst, hunger, and asphyxia.

Previously the subject only witnessed the burial of his double, being himself alive and unburied. The double's burial served only the function of an "affective test." The real self remained outside the coffin.

This phobia implies the horrors of slow asphyxia endured in a state of total helplessness. Abandonment is carried out in its most cruel form. Only primary anxiety could suggest such terrible themes.

We can mention now in a documentary way a sad phenomenon of which the reader has probably thought: suicide following the death of a most beloved person. I know of only one child and two young people, one on his twentieth birthday, who committed suicide on the grave of their mothers.[3] These actions, because carried out, are clearly psychotic in nature.

74. Seeking Refuge in Death and the Abandonee's Masochism

The above-described fantasies have paradoxical functions. Their apparent meaning is to put love to trial, and the daydreamer seeks visible, audible, and undoubted proofs of this love. However, these proofs rest on a false basis. This basis is masochism, or better, a masochistic conception of love life. In such dream productions, masochistic tendencies and love are intermingled. Death is called for as the symbol of ideal love while, in reality, it is the negation of living love. The masochistic abandonee's tendencies falsify the basis and the value of all

---

[3] Let us recall the faithful dogs who refuse to leave their masters' graves and starve to death.

things they inspire. In these fantasies nothing is in its proper place.[4]

This applies also to a second form which these tendencies can assume. This form consists not in daydreams but in acts; in "intensely lived and acted-out fantasies." More precisely, these manifestations are paroxysmal attacks which, like earthquakes, periodically shake the affective life of certain patients overcome by a sudden passionate longing for a state of perfect bliss after they have experienced increasing disappointments and worries.

Indeed, the masochism characteristic of certain abandonees is not limited to dreams and fantasies. It is also translated to the level of social action and manifests itself in particular behavior patterns. We have already mentioned a minor form: sulking with all the refusals, renouncements and privations it implies and inflicts. The child who deprives himself of sweets and desserts to punish his parents is already an abandonee. We frequently find him among our patients.

In the major forms of acting and living out, the subject adopts an attitude which is the reverse of sulking. Instead of silence, we see most noisy demonstrations; and instead of withdrawal, open agitation.

The clearest and most frequent examples are provided by women, usually by wives or lovers. It is obvious that the masochistic crises are related to love conflicts and to the difficulties of sexual life.

---

[4] The term "masochism" is here not used for the body of sexual perversions described and lived by Masoch. Here it defines a quite different idea, the concept of mental or moral masochism emphasized by Freud. This is an attitude in which the subject always mixes pain with joy, suffering with pleasure. In his eyes all that goes well "goes too well" and becomes suspect and a source of worry. In short, things go well when they go wrong. A healthy and complete happiness is not considered as such but as being a source of unhappiness. On this point the mentality of the masochist joins that of the superstitious person. Both confuse two contradictory orders of affective values. This is why they attribute so much importance to annoyances and defeats and less importance to what they have than to what they don't have. Pleasure is bad; it only arouses the sense of impending catastrophe and renders it more acute.

However, men are not exempt from such attacks and excesses. Either because of their temperaments or because of their masculine narcissism, they more rarely use this type of masochism and it is usually milder. More aggressive by nature, they prefer, so to speak, frontal attacks to side attacks. From a clinical viewpoint, however, the abandonee's masochism is not strictly feminine; it is neurotic and as such can affect both sexes.

To illustrate this point, I will take the example of a married couple consisting of a masochistic wife and an apparently normal, although not absolutely faithful, husband. For a few months, with the hypersensitive antennae of the abandonee, the wife has perceived through certain clues that her position in her husband's emotional life has not been as exclusive as she had thought, that is, has not excluded other, more or less short-lived and innocent relationships. Her feeling of security becomes gradually impaired and is replaced by suspicion which, in turn, produces the dysfunctional syndrome of the ego. The absolute love of her husband has turned into a relative one. This deep disturbance of her emotional balance leads first to the compulsion to complain and to recall the happy past; then come revendications and recriminations; finally she resorts to threats. However, these threats are not the ones which normal women instinctively use when they believe themselves abandoned or betrayed. They are of a very different kind, and specifically those of abandonees.

Unfortunately, the results of such a procedure are never good and often quite contrary to the patient's goal. In a few words, we can give the meaning and the spirit of her husband's replies:

"Why nag and cry in such a way. Rather than moving me, these eternal complaints get on my nerves; they don't make me feel any closer; they draw me away from you. In the negative mood we are in now, your complaining leads to nothing. Our 'living together' consists of nothing but complaints and mutual accusations. What's more, I will gladly admit that I am often absent-minded, preoccupied, and cranky; that my work absorbs me and comes first. I know that at times I am unbearable. All right. But don't forget that I respect your rights too [the principle of reciprocity], you are free to seek all the distractions you want, all the pleasures which, I admit, you need so much. I am not as egocentric as you think I am, etc., etc."

This, of course, is another blow! What she needs is not independence, but dependency and mutual possession.

Here is, among others, one of her frequent replies:

"Rights, rights! This is the only word you know. Well, I understand these rights quite differently. The only and true rights of marriage partners worthy of the name are to be all for each other, and one with the other. That is it!"

But the husband feigns deafness to this fundamental and categorical recrimination. He adopts an attitude so terribly objective and relative that it can only pour oil on the fire of an abandoned woman so subjective and absolute in her views.

Between a prelogic and a logic, one as implacable as the other, a progressive divorce is the only outcome. In the end, complaints and demands remain without effect; each succeeding scene ends in a vacuum. The husband no longer listens and is not to be distracted from his personal interests or his outside interests. "False presence" is his ultimate refuge and, unfortunately, it is the perfect method of exasperating the revengeful and aggressive abandonee and driving her into her severest symptoms.

A husband whom one has to share because he "separates himself" is no longer a husband. Too late the wife becomes aware that she has lost the game. Suddenly she realizes the severity of the danger and does not know which action to take. Her growing anxiety will often suggest desperate measures.

Her ultimate resource will be in conformity with her neurosis. The latter will blind her to one essential principle of love life, the same principle which the subjects with the death fantasies ignore. That it is much wiser to try to be loved than to seek pity, far better to move with love than to strike when one has such a great desire to be loved—these ideas are alien to masochistic abandonees.

Cornered, the wife will resort to "the great masochistic scene" typical of the abandonee. Renouncing accusations, she will accuse herself; instead of recriminating against her tired and irritable husband, she will turn the invectives against herself. Under the influence of anxiety, she will let herself utter words which I will try to condense. While we read them, we can see that anxiety can lead those whom it overcomes to the limits of truth and falsehood, of decency and indecency.

"Life is hard and cruel. I am tired, tired. All I do leads to nothing. Am I truly unable to understand anything? I finally believe it. I, who love you so, I see now all the harm I do to you. You are right to hate me because I only bring unhappiness to you. You and the children are miserable and unhappy and I more so than you. How is it possible to make beloved people suffer so much? I realize it now; I am miserable, a horrible and evil human being. If only I could disappear forever and deliver you from my presence . . . Death for me is the only solution, and just you wish it . . . Oh, relax, it will come soon, all will be over for good. You finally will have peace. Death is my last refuge . . ."

It would be wrong to see in these bitter words a sort of blackmail through suicidal threats. The deep suffering they express excuses their intensity and exaggeration. But then, what are they? Why, with what secret aim is death called for so loudly? In reality this call for death is more a call for love.

Hearing these tormented outcries, the wise listener soon realizes their deeper meaning. He guesses that the one who expresses herself in this manner by no means expects to be encouraged and answered: "Maybe . . . after all, you are right. This could perhaps be the best solution . . . go ahead and kill yourself." On the contrary, what she expects is the helpful hand to pull her back from the abyss. What she wishes is to be reassured on one burning point, to know whether or not her life and feelings still have some value for her husband and her family. If, yes, she only wishes to live; if, no, only death can deliver her from her torment. Asecurity cannot be tolerated in life.

In the last analysis, what the masochistic scene demands is not a simple spectator but an active partner. The partner must be the object himself, the unfaithful object, the only one capable of restoring perfect happiness.

However, in her state of masochistic trance, the abandonee plays a double game which owes its ambiguity to the insoluble conflict between a frustrated need for love and an extremely deep resentment; in brief, the conflict between love and hate. The object of all this accumulated aggression is the partner who has not understood or not been able to satisfy the demand for absolute love.

Thus every invective is at the same time an appeal; each complaint a demand; each imprecation, a supplication; each self-accusation, an indirect accusation of the partner with the aim of making him contrite. Her own contrition is a way of condemning him without allowing him to appeal. While beating her own chest, it is his chest that she aims at. These processes are so intricate, and the values so deviant from their original aims that humility and hurt pride are entangled and confused in an inextricable whole.

But what is the patient's ultimate and hidden goal which she attempts to reach through these extreme actions? She is asking for a masochistic affective participation of the partner.

Previously, I have tried to depict the negative attitude of the husband who does not give in, that is, does not participate in the sense of a regressed and infantile acceptance.

The more or less conscious desire of these abandonees is to induce the object to imitate them, and to go through a similar affective masochistic participation. This is the magical power they attribute to the emotional intensity of their laments, to the sinister and threatening character of their outcries.

In many instances, I have seen such contagions, especially if the object is of a sensitive disposition or does not have a clear conscience, or more so if he himself has a tendency for abandonism. In all of us there remains something of this prelogical concept of affective relationships. However, we are not interested in the partner and his own emotional reactions. For us only the masochistic way in which he can react to the masochistic attack of his partner is important. This reaction is identification, the result of an acute crisis of induced adualism.

Following in his wife's footsteps, the object begins to accuse himself, which is an indirect way of accusing her of having let herself go in such an indecent and antisocial attack. Following her example, he in turn uses a sort of moral boomerang. He recognizes his faults (who doesn't have some!) and finally takes all the blame upon himself. He goes as far as to blacken himself in order to whitewash his wife, thus relieving her anxiety; and he reaffirms his love which, despite the deceitful appearance, "has not changed."

Having gone through a whole gamut of emotions, from stupefaction to compassion, from regret to repentance, and from anger to fear, he finally ends up by heaping reproaches upon himself in the same ambiguous, more or less sincere, morbid, and regressive fashion.

Many children resort to the same procedure, especially the child who has been told too often by his anxious mother: "You hurt me so much; you cause me so much sorrow; you are killing me." (Meaning "and afterward, you will be sorry all your life.")

The point is that the husband's brusque contrition, be it more or less sincere, normal or pathological, stops the wife's crisis. A sovereign therapeutic remedy, it cures the symptoms instantaneously. From then on, the roles are reversed. The wife now seeks to comfort the husband. All is forgiven and she now strives to restore his security and self-esteem. Fulfilling this beneficial role is the best way for her to revalue herself. All her hope now lies in the near restoration of their complete unity, based upon an affective participation where each participates in the value and love of the other. Once more, each will be all for the other and nothing without the other.

Thus again, masochism has triumphed over the logic of relationships and over the logic of moral relations. Having taken the road of self-depreciation and self-hate, the husband exempts his wife from the need of going to the end of this road herself. But if the husband refuses to take this road, if he even demands that his wife seek therapy, then the crisis will follow its course until the energy at the disposal of the masochistic tendencies is exhausted or until anxiety has died out.

In the first situation (husband compliant), we can say that the crisis has achieved its goal, has even overshot it. But the goal is not really worth it. One individual has striven to devalue another individual through devaluing himself. In turn, the second individual has devalued himself in order to revalue the first. All this does not ring true because it is determined by a neurotic externalism. No normal person would agree to play this role or have another play it. He would be too well aware of violating two principles to which every evolved person is strongly attached: respect for others and respect for himself. Masochism is always a sin against self-respect.

In the second case (refractory husband), the crisis has failed to achieve its goal. It will most certainly be followed by others. We can imagine into what a blind alley such repetition will lead the marital and familial life.

Everything considered, despite its seeming innocuousness, the abandonee's masochism is dangerous. It is terribly destructive and negative in nature as well as in social consequences. It has the power of contaminating the environment by spreading the germ of false values among the family. In a word, it expresses revenge rather than remorse and expiation. It reveals its characteristic mechanism: the turning against oneself of the hatred accumulated against the object who has violated the pact; and all this with the sole aim of regaining the object's love and of changing this malevolent person back into a benevolent human being.

75. Masochism and Magic Thinking

I have often pointed out the prelogical connection between psychic masochism and magic thinking. From childhood on the masochist has developed the belief that his idea-feelings, his attitudes, and reactions are contagious. In fact, he seeks to exert this "power of influence" over his environment, and he is able to exert it successfully with individuals inclined to excessive scrupulosity or guilt feelings and even more so on individuals with unconscious masochistic tendencies or latent abandonism.

One of my patients let himself, so to speak, become contaminated once a month when his wife had her monthly menstrual attack of masochism. "When my wife becomes depressed before her menses, I become depressed too; when migraine and cramps follow, it is as if I were going to have them too . . . and often I get them." Another patient was taking medications without conviction or necessity, nor did he believe in them; he was taking them solely to please his wife. Finally, however, he started believing in their efficacity. "She would say, 'The doctor advised me to take this; you should try it too.'" He would try, and the medications he took had the magic power of calming his wife and of rendering more effective the numerous remedies she would take as soon as he took them too. To her, a "double cure" had necessarily to be more helpful than her treatment alone.

In certain families one can find several "inductees" grouped around one influential "inductor." I have observed the case of a forever complaining old lady, living with her married daughter, who attracted and shut everybody, mother, father, and two daughters, into the closed circle of their mutual and reciprocal lamentations. From the time she moved in, family life unfolded and exhausted itself under the rule of recrimination disguised as contrition. The grandmother's illness had spread to become the illness of the whole family. Dejected people often depress others.

THE COUVADE

I want to mention briefly this singular custom. Couvade occurs not only in primitive societies but is also used by inhabitants of certain remote mountain valleys. During the pains of labor and until delivery, the husband has to lie beside his wife imitating her wails and echoing her screams. In his mind, this identification has the power of really and physically alleviating the suffering of the woman in labor. It is far from being only a pantomime.

ALGOLAGNIC PARTICIPATION[5]

Sympathy usually exerts a beneficial effect which is purely emotional and magically relieves physical suffering. In couvade, as in other identifications of the same type, the emotional and the physical aspects are confused; there is no distinction between the physiological way of expressing a pain and the subjective fact of experiencing it; no distinction between the cry and the sensation which produces it. These prelogical confusions are the rule in children. In both cases, there is the adualism between the sign and the thing signified.

In the above-mentioned examples, psychic phenomena, like sympathy, are converted into physical phenomena such as cries and disturbances of somatic functions. These cases can be grouped under the name of "painful participation." We will reserve the term of "algolagnic participation" to the phenomena which remain inside the psychic sphere. This term defines the state of a subject, the inducted or "identified," who takes as his own and feels as his own the psychic suffering of another person, the inductor or "identifier." Actually, both processes are closely related; all somatic identifications imply, and result from, a psychic identification.

The most striking example of masochistic identification has been described above. This is the example of the troubled husband who begins to imitate his wife when she falls into a state of trance; who makes himself the echo of her terrible outcries and refutes one after the other of her self-accusations. And what does he do as a good partner that is different from a psychic couvade? As we see, these two processes are good counterparts.

Their dangers are obvious. Of what help is the identified finally to the identifier? Is he not more harmful than helpful when he enters into the mechanism of the neurosis?

[5] *Algolagnia* is a morbid pleasure in the pain either of oneself or others.

To share a neurosis is to render it incurable. At times however it is very difficult not to give in to the direct or indirect appeals of abandonees. All of them have the same fundamental and imperious need to have their idea-feelings, their concepts, and their emotions shared by their environment. To this end, they often use deceit as much as candor. The reason for this is simple. In the last analysis, abandonism, ignoring the laws of psychological evolution, is based on the principle of affective participation. This is why these patients are destined to so much suffering, going from disillusion to disillusion. Affective participation per se can only be precarious and short-lived causing a nonevolved individual vainly to attempt to render identical what is different.

However, neither do his disappointments nor his sorrows have the power to abolish his infantile and tenacious demand that he be able to cause and maintain ideo-affective participation in other individuals. And if he cannot reach his goal in and through happiness, he will do it in and through misfortune. In fact, the abandonee is rarely happy and satisfied; he usually feels unhappy and betrayed and has felt so since childhood. The origin and persistence of his masochism stem from this unhappiness, as do the frequent algolagnic participations in his life. To let oneself be moved by these demands actually harms the subject. To answer a regression with a similar regression is to aggravate the evil one tries to fight. To identify masochistically with an unhappy individual is like pouring oil on a defective lamp. It would be better to replace the wick. Experience shows that only a healthy individual can be loved healthily.

76. From King Oedipus to Little Orestes

Oedipus was blinded for having killed his father, King Laios. For having assassinated his mother, Queen Clytemnestra, who had abandoned him, Orestes was struck by madness. The Erynnies, the Furies whose snakes hissed at his ears, pursued him. He could neither sleep nor rest. The exasperated goddesses demanded punishment for the matricide. Soiled by the blood of his mother, he must pay for his crime with his own blood. The most sacred of ties is the one between mother and child created before birth and surviving death. Blood for blood—such is the law of Apollo.

The passionate love of Electra for her younger brother, Orestes, and the touching affection of the brother for his older sister are well known. Inspired by his poetical and psychological genius, Sophocles has immortalized this reciprocal and truly unique love which was based upon the deep-seated attraction that binds together these two children abandoned by a vicious and criminal mother. In his *Electra,* Sophocles has dramatized a theme familiar to analysts. In this drama the atrocious character of Oedipus's crime has been singularly surpassed. The overemphasis on the horror of matricide indicates Sophocles' deep psychological sense. Considering the two natural relationships, father-child and mother-child, the perversion of the second is the more hateful and ominous.

Clytemnestra had decided to kill her last child after his birth. The nurse was able to save the child from death in substituting her own child for him. Twenty years later, moved by a murderous intent, Orestes secretly comes back to his father's palace in Mycena. He returns not as a culprit but to do justice. "His filial hatred has armed his arm" and he is going to show to men the punishment which the gods reserve for the wicked. Wickedness calls for wickedness; but the law of the talion does not have the power of delivering the wicked from remorse. It has to bow to the stronger law of abandonment.

The matricide accomplished, Orestes flees like a criminal but also like an abandoned child. In his fantasies he sees the shadow of his mother with the Furies and their horrible snakes hissing around them. He wanders from country to country, like a madman, harassed by the goddesses. These represent his own hallucinations or, perhaps, figures in his own dreams. In demanding his death, they symbolize the idea of death, the very desire of the matricidal child to die also, to join his dead mother. One of the most moving themes of the drama is that of the double death.

At other times, the hero is haunted by the living image of his mother, of his mother returned from death to life having been absolved from her crime by death. These contradictory fantasies have the same function: to re-establish the tie between mother and child, the most natural bond and the one that can least be broken. In therapy we find that these macabre themes reappear in the dreams of the modern prototypes of Orestes.

In *Electra*, Sophocles uses another interesting device.

"What is so particularly striking in Sophocles' play? One thinks of the narration of the imaginary death of Orestes in the Delphic games without forgetting that in this narration, which is one of the main parts of the drama, the poet has told us that everything is imaginary from the first to the last word. There is something extraordinary about this. The narration is full of colorful, precise and picturesque details. Let us be carried away by the inspiration of the narrator, and let not the rude suspicion of a lie enter our minds; we are in the theater where all is imagined, even that which is true."[6]

We can understand that a well-known Hellenist and student of Sophocles invites his readers not to confuse fantasy and lie. To analysts such a recommendation would be superfluous. They know that the human being finds his most intimate truth in his

---

[6] P. Masqueray: *Sophocles. Les Belles Lettres*, Paris, 1929, Vol. I, p. 205.

imaginary productions, daydreams or night dreams, and that he expresses it with the utmost sincerity through these media. Following Masqueray in his literary analysis, we find that it leads him, and us, to a new and astonishing fact.

Going to Mycena with his inseparable Pylades before the matricide, Orestes has taken great care to carry with him a brazen urn. However, this funeral urn contains no ashes. He hides it behind bushes while waiting to realize his strange plan. Later the acme of the drama will occur when the two friends enter the scene in the presence of Electra, unrecognized by her, while two servants follow, one carrying the funeral urn.

Then in her anguished and celebrated effusions of fraternal love, sure that the ashes of her beloved brother have been brought back to the royal grave, Electra speaks to an empty urn.

Is there in any drama a situation more artificial and hazardous? Again it is important not to think. If we think for one moment that Orestes who is alive enters the scene purposively to provoke the excruciating farewell from his sister, the illusion is destroyed and, far from sharing Electra's sorrow, we will be tempted to tell her about her error and thus end it.[7]

"This does not in any way diminish our emotion because Sophocles has made it so exquisite. However, in one detail he may be going too far. Orestes precedes the servant who holds the urn and risks a few, ambiguous words where he alludes to his situation—a strange one, indeed, as he is the companion of the man who is believed to carry his, Orestes', ashes. Here again the ability of the poet is a little baffling. We accept the deception and even wish to be deceived, but without being told about it."[8]

[7] *Ibid.*, p. 206. The analyst would not commit such a mistake.

[8] Concerning this theatrical trick, some people have thought it good or moving lyricism—others, like Goethe, if I am not mistaken, have found it to be in poor taste and ringing a false note in the poetic harmony of a masterpiece.

The ambiguous words of Orestes are:

"Who amongst you will tell the people of the palace that the one who is awaited is here with those who accompany him?"

Here are some excerpts of the celebrated lament of Electra:

"His dust lies there. Please give it to me, sir. I want to hold it in my hands and weep—weep over his dust and remember with tears all my sorrow and the sorrow of all my house . . .

"So here is all that is left of my beloved Orestes; only this to remember you by, my dearest on earth. . . . My poor darling, death lay in the way you had to walk and I must die, must die with your death. Oh, my brother! Let me come home with you, dead with the dead, to stay with you forever."

Once more the poet refers to the double death.

Later a dialogue ensues. Orestes has recognized his sister because of the "excess of her sorrows."

ORESTES: Give me back the urn—then I will tell you everything.

ELECTRA: No, no, for pity's sake, don't ask me to do that.

ORESTES: Do as I say. Believe me, it will be best.

ELECTRA: The only thing I love. Have pity, sir. Don't take it from me.

ORESTES: I cannot let you keep it.

ELECTRA: Oh, I am never to lay you in your grave, Orestes beloved.

ORESTES: You speak too rashly, lady; this is no time for funerals.

ELECTRA: No time? My brother dead—

ELECTRA: Is it really you? Oh, light! Oh, joy!

ORESTES: I share it.

ELECTRA: Is this indeed your voice again?

ORESTES: Ask for no other witness.

ELECTRA: Your hand in mine?

ORESTES: Forever.[9]

[9] *Electra*, by Sophocles, translated by E. S. Watling, Penguin Classics.

Thus we are led back to the theme of "life in common." Even though it might seem an affront to dramatic art, let us transcribe this scene in terms of the abandonee's psychology. Psychology might have inspired the poet, as it has inspired others as great as Sophocles.

All through this heart-rending scene, Orestes, the most illustrious of all abandonees, is doing nothing but assisting at his own funeral and thus putting his sister's love to trial. And all this for Electra, the only woman who loves him and whom he can love! Does not her love substitute for the maternal love which a criminal mother had refused to her son?

With perfect artistic skill, Sophocles lets us assist in the revaluation of Orestes through the love of his sister; the brother wins back that which the son, completely devalued by the betrayal of his mother, had lost. Besides revalorizing her beloved brother, Electra replaces the anxiety in his tormented soul by security, faith and strength; she is able to make an autonomous man of him. Orestes, now sure of the love and support of his sister, becomes fiercely determined to execute his criminal and vengeful plans. An unworthy mother has to die; having been replaced in his affection, there is no longer a place on earth for her.

Thus the funeral song of a live woman enchants a "dead" man. Affective psychology, if not poetic art, authorizes such a freedom of expression. It invites us to fantasy in the place of Orestes. To him, it is not a funeral song but a love song capable of evoking rapture and joy in the abandonee who only aspires for new life. This resurrection is the work of Electra's demonstrations of love, which owe their magic power to their exalting and acutely painful, "affectively absolute" character. Orestes could hardly remain deaf to such a pathetic "appeal" and "unique welcome." There could not be more complete "affective

presence." Love abolishes death, even more defies and denies it.
From life to death, from death to life, this is the device of the
fraternal love conceived in grief and cherished despite the definitive separation implied by the supposed death.

Thanks to his macabre trick—I could say thanks to his
fantasy—Orestes is overwhelmed with love. The dialogues of
which we have quoted parts are invaluable documents. Their
exalted poetry is evidence of one of the abandonees' special
traits: *their affective avidity,* as it seeks its way and justification
in the conclusion of apodictic pacts. In this respect, Sophocles
is a great clinician.

CONCLUSIONS

The fundamental principle of the death fantasies

In this chapter I have attempted to describe the most typical
forms of death fantasies. We can now delineate their common
principle which consists in a particular confusion. The subject
confuses two situations, A and B.

A. In the first situation we have two human beings separated
by space.

B. In the second, we have a live person and a dead person,
separated by death.

Death is thus reduced to a pure question of space.

This prelogical conception, as we know, is characteristic of
the child. Its presence or recurrence in death fantasies of the
adult is sufficient to prove the regressed character and the origin
of these imaginary productions inspired or determined by very
infantile needs.

With this confusion, death has lost the meaning of a fatal
and irreparable catastrophe. The subject is no longer powerless
when confronted with it; he is stronger than "fatality" and able
to overcome the worst calamity that can befall him. He

triumphs over separation through death as he triumphs over separation through space. He uses identical means to abolish both of them with the help of magic thinking.

The most decisive way to abolish distance is reunion. Let us put ourselves in Electra's place after she has been heart-broken by the death of her father. Let us read again the pathetic out-cries of the orphaned daughter spoken to the ghost of Agamemnon. Later the desperate daughter gives way to the desperate sister. Her appeals to the ghost of her brother have the same character as the appeals to her father's ghost. The father was the "first object"; the brother is "the second object," the substitute object, able to undo the abandonment and to attenuate the intolerable suffering it provoked. As soon as she cries out, Orestes returns from the realm of death with an empty urn. He comes back, dead and alive at the same time. Alive and full of youth and love, Orestes carries the urn in which lie the "ashes" of the dead Orestes!

77. THE FUNDAMENTAL CONFLICT

THE RETURN TO THE MALEVOLENT AND BENEVOLENT "GREAT BEINGS"

After having insisted on the theme, "from life to death," we can now emphasize the reverse theme, "from death to life," and thus conclude on a less gloomy note.

There is a charm that ties love to death; the charm is dis-astrous if death means the loss of love; it is comforting when it has the meaning of a return to the sphere of eternal love. For the abandonee the experience of death becomes crucial because it is assimilated in the experience of love. We saw that this fantasy derives from the myth of the return to the far or lost mother and to her womb.

However, it is important to bring these poetical interpretations to the level of psychology. Until now, I have attempted to clarify the magic function of the idea or the feeling of death for the abandonee. The idea-feeling of death constantly reappears in his dreams and fantasies. I have called this function, negative or nefarious.

On the other hand, I have pointed out the inverse function of positive and beneficial magic thinking, insisting upon the fact that it has a regenerating power in being the only thing able to annul the deadly power of its opposite, the negative function. This is why the anxious patient, struggling against his suffering, resorts to it. There is no other way out of the dark labyrinth where they are held and led astray by nefarious magic thinking.

We can recall here the dream of Ariane with its pagan and benevolent god, the giant dominating the black ocean and saving Ariane from drowning and death. In the course of analysis, one often observes similar dreams; these are the favorable and beneficent dreams opposed to the malevolent and destructive nightmares.

In general, these good dreams correspond to an improvement in the neurosis; at least they characterize its "good phases." In turn, nightmares accompany the resurgences of anxiety which revive the images of the old malevolent beings.

The following examples are what I will call "typical scenes" and are related to the two opposite types of dreams just mentioned: those permeated by a malevolent power or transfigured by a benevolent one.

A. THE THEME OF THE CLIFF

"I find myself hanging over a cliff . . . or clinging to its edges . . . The tree (or rock) on which I am hanging starts to bend, is uprooted, comes loose . . . I am going to fall . . . Just as I fall, I awaken."

Such a dream has often been interpreted as a suicidal theme; however, the origin of the drama is not so simple. Questioning the patient more closely, one finds that some other person participates in the mortal accident as if he had conceived or managed it. He is the moving spirit of the dream. He can precipitate the fatal ending, or he can also prevent and stop the fall. During therapy and because of the transference, the analyst sooner or later becomes this person.

"My dream took place in a tree bent over a precipice . . . You are sitting on one branch and hold me over the abyss by one foot. I am very much afraid that you will drop me . . ."

This dream alluded to an impending interruption of the patient's analysis. Unconsciously and as a rule, every separation from the analyst, even a brief interruption of treatment will be interpreted as an abandonment.

In these examples a frightening person initiates a disaster from which this person himself escapes. In other dreams he may also be a victim and share the fate of the dreaming subject (the theme of a common death).

"I am with my mother in a sort of cable-car cabin. We go downwards with greater and greater speed . . . as if the cable had been broken . . ." The subject wakes up, certain of the catastrophe but before it has actually taken place. The theme of such dreams is double death. Older anxiety-producing fears are here expressed through the idea or the vision of a catastrophe: on one hand, the child's or the adolescent's fear of death which he has experienced many times; on the other hand, the fear of the mother's death. The double accident takes on the meaning of a definitive solution which will put an end to the longlasting torment.

B. THE THEME OF THE CAVERN OR THE OBSTRUCTED TUNNEL

A young Parisian, very attached to his mother, is sent to England on a new job.

He dreams: "In a tunnel, it must be the tunnel under the Channel . . . the light is dim . . . I am in a kind of street-car automobile. . . . my mother is driving. The tunnel becomes narrower and narrower. Finally we touch a wall which closes off the narrow passage. We are blocked; there is no way out. Mother makes a sign which means: No, I will not leave you here all alone; I will stay with you."

This narrow cavern where one cannot breathe is the symbol of the grave. The refusal to separate from the mother and the implied wish for a double death to overcome the separation are expressed clearly. This symbolism is similar to the one of the "cave" and the narrow passageway where one cannot breathe. All these themes are inspired by anxiety.

C. THE THEME OF THE PIT AND THE QUICKSAND

"I am lying in a sort of narrow pit . . . Filled with horror, I struggle to move and get out. But somebody stronger than I holds me motionless. At every effort on my part, he brutally throws me back to the ground and paralyzes all my movements . . . as if he wanted to bury me for good."

"My feet are caught in quicksand. I cannot move them any more . . . somebody is weighing upon me with all his strength pushing me down more and more. I become gradually engulfed in the sand, panic-stricken and powerless."

D. THE AMBIGUOUS SYMBOLS

These are objects, characters, situations, or attributes which have a double function, both life-bringing and death-dealing:

A. To conserve and spread life, increase strength and power, or assure happiness.

B. To weaken, poison, or kill.

Such symbols with their two opposite meanings are known not only in psychology but are also found in myths and folklore.

Among others we have: the *snake-phallus,* the *kiss-bite,* the *bee-scorpion,*[10] and the *cradle-coffin.*

The following dream uses another symbol: the *spoon-gun.*

Paul, the oldest of many children, has to stay in town alone in order to prepare for some examinations while the rest of his family has gone to the country to spend their vacation in a pleasant summer home. The place is located in a part of France renowned for its good food. Paul either has to prepare his meals himself or to eat alone in a restaurant.

He dreams: "I am in our old apartment but I have to escape because the people who are after me are roaming around. I take refuge in a restaurant. The only free table is occupied by dogs which I chase away. At this same moment somebody enters suddenly and points a spoon at me. But there is a gun hidden under the spoon and he shoots and kills me."

The old apartment is where his brothers and sisters were born in rapid succession. At the arrival of each of them, Paul suffered a sense of abandonment. He acquired a gloomy, difficult and jealous character. The new babies monopolized the mother. "Everything is for them."

Lack of food and loneliness are nearly synonymous. Or, in Paul's case, the absence of their cook was equated with the absence of the nursing mother, the worst of all loneliness. To have to buy one's own food and prepare one's meals is a symbol of abandonment. Paul lost his appetite. This is to say that he

---

10 The famous "black widow spider" is a favored symbol and often represents the "bad mother" in nightmares. In legends it is the typical malevolent animal.

would have a big appetite if he could be with his family in their summer residence and could taste the fine meals prepared by his mother.

In the past, he had watched jealously while the mother breast-fed or *spoon*-fed the babies with never-ending patience. The love and tenderness of the mother while she cares for the baby gives rise in the baby to the first notion of an "absolute bond," the first feeling of an affective presence. In this way originate the symbolic relationships: to be fed equals to be loved; food equals presence; not to be fed equals separation and absence. In contrast, the mother who feeds brothers and sisters while she lets you perish with sorrow (and unconsciously, with hunger) simply is a mother who kills, who does not care to know if you have or have not had enough to eat.

The people who are after me. This group of enemies condenses everything into one: the mother and all the siblings which she has successively preferred and favored. They are the "gang of persecutors." In the dream they objectify the fear and the aggressiveness of the dreamer. They are also represented by the "bad dogs," the enraged pack which chases and persecutes. Paul finds them also in the restaurant, sharing and occupying the only free table in order to *prevent him from taking his meal.* Paul is condemned to starve. However, full of revolt, he has the courage to chase them away. But, as soon as he has committed this crime—surely a heinous crime in his mother's eyes—he has to bear the deserved punishment. This episode shows how much he has resented those voracious dogs!

The mother can no more tolerate his gesture of hate than she has been able to tolerate Paul's previous aggressive reactions to the younger children when he was smaller. Too often she had to intervene and punish him severely. However, she committed a disciplinary error in that she sent him to bed without his meals or banished him from the family table where his rivals were triumphing.

The analysis of the dream brought back many other painful memories. Heartbreaks were the rule during Paul's childhood. He was even threatened with a reformatory ruled by terrifying fathers. Around the age of six or seven he became "impossible." Then fate played its role and forced the mother to carry out her thoughtless threats. The child's health was declining, he had lost weight, had bronchitis repeatedly, had ganglions, and other symptoms. To prevent a possible tuberculosis, he was finally "sent away" to a children's home in the mountains. There under the rule of a very strict and punitive matron, he went through his great crisis of abandonment.

THE THEME OF THE DANGEROUS BRIDGE

"There is a very high bridge which I have to cross . . . but I become frightened because . . ." Various interpretations can follow: the bridge is not strong, it is slippery, shaky, has no railing, is broken in the middle, etc. Below the bridge, deep down, there is an abyss or water (the dark water which attracts and engulfs). Falling is certain if the dreamer, trying to face the danger, attempts to cross the bridge.

Besides himself, someone else is always present: at times, the promoter of the accident (who forces the dreamer to cross the bridge with him), at times the protector who, while crossing the bridge, repairs it or otherwise averts all danger so that the fall into the abyss is avoided.

A bridge is a creation of scientific knowledge and rational technique. It corrects nature. Besides this universal meaning, the bridge has various symbolic meanings, especially during the course of analysis. One of them, conceived of by the ego, is related to treatment. It implies the idea of overcoming an obstacle, of reaching the other side (the adult side), gaining the possession of security and the rights of autonomy, becoming free from the past and from childhood. In short, it expresses the idea of healing.

There is, however, an opposite meaning: the bridge which becomes dangerous and deadly for the dreamer who crosses it. Here nefarious thinking intervenes. The fear of the future predominates, increased and exaggerated by the loss of security due to the "unknown." "I do not quite know what to expect on the other side of this bridge which both attracts and repels me. On this side, at least, I know what I have and am assured. I have my husband and my analysis, at least some security!"

The dangerous bridge is the concrete expression of the danger of losing the feeling of security. And at the same time it symbolizes the fundamental conflict between intelligent and phobic thinking, between the rational and the irrational thinking of the abandonee, between the scientific method (the therapy) and the neurosis. In short, this is the conflict between logic and prelogic. No synthesis is possible between these two antithetic forms of thought.

NOTES ON "CORRECTED DREAMS"

This is the name I give to certain particular dreams where one can see the intervention of rational thinking before the dramatic ending of the dream scene. Rational thinking aims at correcting the processes and tricks of magic thinking by baffling them. It is akin to the phenomenon mentioned in Section 24 where the dreamer in his dream is aware of dreaming. Just as the idea of dreaming can be introduced into the dream itself, so logical thinking can also become manifest in it. Reassuming its functions and rights, it then intervenes and opposes prelogical magic thinking. For example:

"High up in the mountains I am on a very steep path down which come cascades of rocks. I can neither climb further nor go down and am overwhelmed by dizziness and intense fear. But suddenly the scenery changes. I am comfortably seated in a cable-car which brings me to the summit. Having regained my composure, I say to myself: That cable-car is just a trick, and not such a clever one at that! You just wanted to escape your fear and avoid the effort, like poor mountaineers do."

The cable-car has a double use: on one hand, it suppresses primary anxiety and prevents the imminent and certain catastrophe; on the other hand, it avoids an effort which would be a problem.

In reality, the patient's problem is to overcome the intense fear inspired by his father whom he sees as a malevolent being. What is so striking here is the intervention in the dream of self-criticism. This rational, and so to speak, psychoanalytic judgment on the trickery of the dream is due to an advance in his analysis. This progress is proof of a change in the deeper ego structure. A new zone has been formed to correct the activity of the contact zone. And interestingly enough, it is able to function during and despite sleep.

A kind of syllogism will summarize the thoughts apparent in this dream. (1) I wish to be freed from anxiety and the unhappy (evil) thoughts which provoke anxiety. In order to achieve this I only have to call for benevolent thinking (the cable-car). (2) But ... those are children's tricks. I should have persevered and reached the top through my own forces. (3) Thus, my anxiety is not invincible as I had imagined, and the ideas which arouse it are absurd.

78. The Benevolent Genius

Fortunately black magic is not the only kind of magic. There also exists the "white" or "pink" magic which surrounds the first years of happy children. In line with our terminology, this is "benevolent magic."

As expected, the benevolent being is the opposite of the malevolent being, and it is easy to foresee what his functions are. He averts threats, saves the subject from mortal dangers, finds a way out of blocked tunnels, gets one out of traps, pits, caves, and crevices. In a word, he defeats the grave.

In general, the benevolent being appears in the dreams of patients during the resolution phase of treatment.

"I am lying flat on the edge of a high cliff. Far down, I see the ocean agitated as in a tempest. A very strong wind pushes me downwards, and I slowly glide toward the abyss. But the scenery changes. I am at the bottom of the cliff, safe and healthy. Someone is here, my companion, and he smiles at me. I know that he has saved me."

Be he called companion, guardian angel, or friend, the function of the benevolent being is always the same: he is the *absolute protector,* the one who dispenses security. His way of intervention sheds additional light on the magic nature of the need for protection in the unconscious; and it also illustrates the tremendous strength which this need derives from abandonment. The function of the absolute protector is magical and proportionate to his capacity to annul the influence of malevolent powers, be they actual objects of nature or imagined.

Here is a war dream:

"We are in a dark underground shelter. Outside there is terrible bombing. Suddenly panic breaks out because one of us is a traitor. But someone says: Don't be afraid of anything; we are safe. And then we are back outside, sitting in the sun. The bombardment is over."

A woman, age thirty-four, in the last phase of treatment, brings the following recurrent dream:

"I speak to somebody who is very wicked . . . a very questionable character ... I know that he has done much harm. He comes nearer. But my anxiety does not last because I know that my friend, the one who protects me, is here somewhere. His presence gives me so much confidence that my eyes stare at the enemy who then becomes smaller and smaller. The friend calls me and makes a date. Later he will tell me where to go." She adds: "I feel that I am very much better, but it is not yet over." The "later" in the dream means that she still expects some advice from her analyst before the separation from him.

At the age of five, this patient was abandoned by her father whom she adored; later she was abandoned a second time by her mother whom she hated, and still later a third time by her husband. She then became depressed. During her analysis, a malevolent being haunted her dreams. At the beginning of her second year of treatment, he became "smaller and smaller" and gave way to the protector-friend. In her late childhood she had already given the "Friend" a place in her stories and fantasies. At all times she used to evoke his presence and protection. Though he was only a fantasy, he had magic powers. When she called for him in difficult moments, for instance, when her mother berated her, he would appear immediately and "arrange everything." She said: "In my life there has always been a good and a bad influence. I know now that the bad influence was my horrible sorrows. But I have had great trouble telling you about the good influence. I was so afraid you might think me ridiculous and crazy, that you might take away my Friend."

CONCLUSION

We have attempted to analyze the origin, the deeper meaning, and the interplay of the infantile mythology to which our patients so fervently cling. The mystery of this interplay is to be found less in the action of magic powers than in their conflicts. Benevolent magic thinking is absolutely opposed to malevolent magic thinking; and in their childhoods our patients have lived daily with this very opposition.

What have we achieved in studying the deep levels on which all contradictions characteristic of abandonees are functionally unified and explained? More light has been shed on the fears, wishes, sufferings, and joys of childhood. More important, we have learned better to understand the genesis, the very essence, I would say, of a very widespread neurosis which is dangerous not only for the patients themselves but also for those in their environment: not only for the "objects" to whom they become attached but also for the "subjects" who become attached to them.

On a deeper level, the essence of this illness is an implacable, inescapable suffering such as experienced by Sophocles' Orestes.

Studying these patients over a long period, one begins to fear that every child who has suffered from primary anxiety will never quite be able to overcome it. The essential data of the drama can be reduced to one extreme antithesis which only exceptionally can be resolved spontaneously. There is an irreducible opposition between affective prelogic and the logic of relationships; between the magic laws of the former and the implacable rational laws of the latter, laws which are too hard or painful for the abandonees to live by. All efforts at reconcilia-

301

tion between these two concepts of relationships in life are the work of the neurosis rather than a cure. All compromises are faulty and give rise to a series of traumas and disappointments.

Our patients constantly confront us with the harshness of this antithesis and betray their powerlessness to overcome it. Insisting on its painful consequences, they endlessly bring us back to the source of their suffering which at times transforms them into angels and at times into devils. They are angels when love gives them security. They are devils when love is withdrawn and this withdrawal changes their existence into a living death, so clearly shown by their fantasies and dreams.

But are they really devils? If one listens to the complaints of their objects, one would have to agree. However, their wickedness is reactive, not inborn; it is due to experience and not to nature. Betrayal inflames it.

Loss of security can drive the gentlest abandonee to the worst kinds of violence. *Asphaleia* can again make a charming and social person of him. The former makes devils, the latter creates angels.

Insecurity is the symbol of death; security the symbol of life.

BIOGRAPHICAL NOTE

Dr. Charles Odier was born in 1888 in Geneva, Switzerland, and died in 1954 in Lausanne. After his medical studies in Geneva he worked as a resident in neurology and psychiatry in Vienna. Following further medical training and general practice he became interested in the study of neurosis. After specialized training at the Berlin Psychoanalytic Institute, he practiced psychoanalysis in Paris where he was a member of the Psychoanalytical Society. In 1939, Dr. Odier returned to Switzerland where much of his time was devoted to the writing of his books. In 1943 he published *Les deux sources consciente et inconsciente de la vie Morale (The Two Sources, Conscious and Unconscious, of Moral Life)*, in 1947 *L'angoisse et la pensée Magique (Anxiety and Magic Thinking)*, and in 1950 *L'Homme esclave de son infériorité. Essai sur la genese du Moi (Man the Slave of His Inferiority. Essay on the Genesis of the Ego)*. He left numerous notes on problems of the inferiority complex and on psychic autonomy. These notes were to be the substance of two further books which his death prevented him from completing.